Advanced FAST TRACK

Bill Coe
Montgomery College

Lisa Lovejoy
Montgomery College

Table of Contents

Elementary Algebra Lessons

Intermediate Algebra

Extra Problem Sets

Appendices

Foreword and Acknowledgments

This workbook was written to support a short course that provides a review of elementary algebra and intermediate algebra topics. The course is designed for students who have had these subjects before. The objective is to save the students time and money by placing them in the appropriate level math course – neither too high nor too low. If we are successful in doing this, we will provide a better learning environment for students and instructors alike.

We had a lot of help in developing this workbook from people at Montgomery College. Thanks go to Professors Jose Alonso and Zdonna Skalsky who spent many hours reviewing drafts. Their comments contributed immensely to this workbook. Thanks also go Professor Fred Katiraie for his support.

Note to the Students

The Advanced Fast Track course is designed to save you time and money by placing you in the highest-level course based on your mastery of the material. Advanced Fast Track is a review course. It reviews Elementary Algebra and Intermediate Algebra concepts. Depending on the scores you achieve on the two tests you take in this course, you will proceed to either Elementary Algebra, Intermediate Algebra or a college level math class.

This workbook has 38 separate lessons and two practice tests. Each lesson has an instructional area followed by some exercises. After the exercises there is an answer section that shows how each of the exercises is done. About midway through the book, there is a practice Elementary Algebra test. Then, near the end of the book, there is a practice Intermediate Algebra test. These tests are similar to the tests you will be given during the course. At the end of the book, there are extra problem sets for each lesson followed by the answers to those problem sets.

To help you along your way there are a number of icons to alert you to important items:

A Rule to Remember!
This icon alerts you of an important rule, property or handy trick to commit to memory.

Check Your Work
The check icon highlights an instance when you can check your own work to ensure you got it right.

Lesson 1: Working with Formulas

Early in the Prealgebra section, we learned how to solve equations that had one variable, or unknown quantity, using the addition and multiplication properties. In this section, we are going to work with equations (actually formulas) that have many unknown quantities. For example, let's look at the distance formula:

Example 1. *distance = rate • time* or $d = r \bullet t$

In this example, we would multiply the **rate** times the **time** to get the **distance**. However, a problem may give us the **distance** and the **rate** and ask us to solve for **time**. We need to be able to manipulate the basic equation from one that tells us what the formula for **distance** is to one that will tell us what **time** is. To do this, we follow the same rules for solving equations that we learned earlier but we will treat t as the unknown. That means that r becomes the coefficient for t and we divide each side by r, and the result is:

$$\frac{d}{r} = \frac{r \bullet t}{r}$$

$$\frac{d}{r} = t$$

Let's try one that is a little more complex, the area of a triangle. The area of a triangle is ½ the base times the height. Let's solve that formula for the height:

Example 2. $A = \frac{1}{2}bh$ Solve for h.

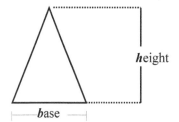

This formula has a fraction in it, ½. In our section on solving equations with fractions, we learned that our first step was to clear the equation of fractions. We do that here by multiplying by 2. Then, we divide by the coefficient of our unknown. Here is how it looks:

$$2 \bullet A = 2 \bullet \frac{1}{2}bh$$

$$2A = bh$$

$$\frac{2A}{b} = \frac{bh}{b}$$

$$\frac{2A}{b} = h$$

Lesson 1: Working with Formulas

The rules we have been following are basically the same ones learned in an earlier section but we will restate them here as they relate to solving a formula for a given variable or letter:

Rules for Solving a Formula for a Given Variable	A Rule to Remember!

Rules for Solving a Formula for a Given Variable

A Rule to Remember!

1. Identify the letter to be solved for.

2. Clear the equation of fractions or decimals.

3. Collect like terms, if necessary.

4. Use the addition property to get all terms with the given letter on one side of the equation and all other terms on the other side.

5. Use the multiplication property so that the given letter has a coefficient of one.

Let's try one more example:

Example 3. $ax + by = c$ Solve for y

$by = c - ax$ Addition property (subtract ax from both sides)

$y = \dfrac{c - ax}{b}$ Multiplication property (divide each side by b)

Now try these

2

Lesson 1: Working with Formulas

Exercises

1. $I = Prt$ Solve for P

2. $y = mx + b$ Solve for b

3. $h = \dfrac{v^2}{2g}$ Solve for g

4. $A = \pi r^2$ Solve for r^2

5. $P = 2l + 2w$ Solve for l.

Solutions

1. $I = Prt$ Solve for P

    $$\frac{I}{rt} = \frac{P\cancel{rt}}{\cancel{rt}}$$

    $$\frac{I}{rt} = P$$

    Since P is the given variable, we want to isolate it on one side and get everything else on the other side. Since P is already on the right side, we'll keep it there. Now we have to get it to stand by itself (have a coefficient of one). Right now it has a coefficient of rt. Therefore, we have to divide each side by that coefficient.

2. $y = mx + b$ Solve for b

    $$y = mx + b$$
    $$\underline{-mx \quad -mx}$$
    $$y - mx = b$$

    To solve for b, we have to subtract mx from each side of the equation.

3. $h = \dfrac{v^2}{2g}$ Solve for g

    $$(2g)h = (\cancel{2g})\frac{v^2}{\cancel{2g}}$$

    $$2gh = v^2$$

    $$\frac{\cancel{2g}h}{\cancel{2}h} = \frac{v^2}{2h}$$

    $$g = \frac{v^2}{2h}$$

    When we have an equation that contains a fraction, we generally want to get rid of the fraction to simplify the math. We do that by multiplying by the common denominator of the fractions in the equation. Since there is only one fraction involved, the common denominator is that denominator (2g).

    This makes the equation much easier to handle. We solve for g by dividing each side by $2h$.

4. $A = \pi r^2$ Solve for r^2

    $$\frac{A}{\pi} = \frac{\cancel{\pi} r^2}{\cancel{\pi}}$$

    $$\frac{A}{\pi} = r^2$$

    Divide by the coefficient (π) of the variable (r^2).

5. $P = 2l + 2w$ Solve for l.

    $$P = 2l + 2w$$
    $$\underline{-2w \qquad -2w}$$
    $$P - 2w = 2l$$
    $$\frac{P - 2w}{2} = \frac{\cancel{2}l}{\cancel{2}}$$
    $$\frac{P - 2w}{2} = l$$

    Isolate the variable term of interest (2l) on the right side by subtracting $2w$ on both sides of the equation. Then, divide each side by the coefficient of l, which is 2.

Lesson 2: Solving Inequalities

For most of mathematics, we are studying equalities – quantities <u>equal</u> to each other. In this section we are going to learn about inequalities. For equations, we use equal signs (=). For inequalities, we use several symbols.

$<$ This symbol means "less than."

$>$ This symbol means "greater than."

$\leq$ This symbol means "less than or equal to."

$\geq$ This symbol means "greater than or equal to."

We use these symbols to indicate the relationship of different quantities. For example, we read $x > 3$ as the quantity x is greater than 3. That means any value of x that is greater than 3 (such as 4, 5, 10, etc.) satisfies this relationship. Similarly, $x \leq 4$ is read as "the quantity x is less than or equal to 4." Some values that satisfy this relationship are 3, 2, 1, -3, -10, etc. In addition, the value 4 satisfies this relationship. Because we can't list all the values that satisfy a relationship, we can express our answers graphically using a number line.

Example 1.   **Graph** $x > 2$

We want to show all values greater than 2. We do that by drawing a line from 2 on the number line to the right. At the start of the line, we use a small open dot, at the end of the line we put an arrow pointing to the right indicating that this solution set continues. Here is how it looks:

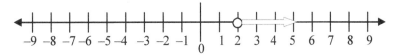

Example 2.   **Graph** $x \leq -2$

In this example, we want to show all values equal to or less than –2. We indicate the "or equal to" part by using a bold dot. Here is how this one looks:

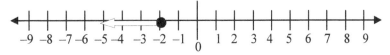

In earlier sections of this book, we learned how to solve equations by using the addition and multiplication properties. We use those same properties to solve inequalities. This means we can add or subtract a number on one side of the inequality as long as we do the same to the other side of the inequality. Also, we can multiply or divide by a number on one side of the inequality as long as we do the same to the other side. **There is one difference when using the multiplication property, which we will discuss, later in this lesson.** For now, let's solve some inequalities using the addition and multiplication properties.

Example 3.   **Solve** $3x + 5 > 11$

$$\begin{array}{r} 3x + 5 > 11 \\ \underline{-5 \quad -5} \\ 3x > 6 \end{array}$$

Solve this by first using the addition property and subtracting 5 from each side of the inequality.

$$\frac{3x}{3} > \frac{6}{3}$$
$$x > 2$$

Next, use the multiplication property by dividing each side by 3.

Lesson 2: Solving Inequalities

Example 4.   **Solve** $2x - 7 \le -3x + 8$

$5x \le 15$

First, we will use the addition property twice to get all the variable terms on the left (add $3x$) and all the constant terms on the right (add 7).

$x \le 3$

Second, we use the multiplication property and divide by 5 so that we are left with the variable with a coefficient of 1,

 A Rule to Remember!   Remember we said there is one difference in solving inequalities using the multiplication property than solving equations. The difference is **when we multiply or divide by a negative number, we reverse the inequality sign.** To see why we do that, consider this inequality:

Example 5. $-5 > -9$

This is a true inequality because –5 is greater than –9.

$$\frac{-5}{-1} > \frac{-9}{-1}$$

Using the multiplication property, let's divide each side by –1

$5 > 9$

$5 < 9$

But, 5 is **not** greater than 9! So, when we multiply or divide by a negative number, we **reverse the inequality** sign to maintain the correct relationship.

Let's apply this to another example.

Example 6.   **Solve** $-6x + 4 \ge 16$

$-6x \ge 12$

Solve by first using the addition property to move the constant term to the right side of the inequality.

$$\frac{-6x}{-6} \ge \frac{12}{-6}$$

$x \le -2$

Now use the multiplication property and divide by –6. When we do this, reverse the direction of the inequality sign.

Example 7.   **Solve** $-7x - 5 > -2x + 15$

Solve by using the addition property twice, once to move the variable term to the left side of the inequality (by adding $2x$), and once to move the constant term to the right side (by adding 5). Using the addition property has no effect on the inequality sign.

$-5x > 20$

Now, divide by –5 and reverse the direction of the inequality sign.

$x < -4$

Are you ready to solve some inequalities?

6

Lesson 2: Solving Inequalities

Exercises

1.   Solve: $5 + 4x < 29$

2.   Solve: $25 \geq 7 + 9x$

3.   Solve: $-6x + 5 < -31$

4.   Solve: $8 - 7y \leq 5 + 3y - 7$

5.   Solve and graph: $3x < x + 4$

6.   Solve and graph: $5y + 7 > -11 - y$

7.   Solve and graph: $2x + 6 \leq 5x$

8.   Solve and graph: $-6x + 2 \geq -2x + 18$

Lesson 2: Solving Inequalities

Solutions

1.   Solve: $5 + 4x < 29$
         $x < 6$

Use the addition property to move the constant term to the right side of the inequality (by subtracting 5 from each side), then use the multiplication property and divide each side by 4.

2.   Solve: $25 \geq 7 + 9x$
         $2 \geq x$
         $x \leq 2$

Subtract 7 from each side and then divide by 9 and the result is $2 \geq x$
The variable on the right side is OK, but we can restate the answer with the variable on the left, but the direction of the inequality changes like.

3.   Solve: $-6x + 5 < -31$
         $x > 6$

Subtract 5 from each side and then divide by –6. Don't forget that when we divide by a negative number we reverse the direction of the inequality sign.

4.   Solve: $8 - 7y \leq 5 + 3y - 7$
         $8 - 7y \leq 3y - 2$ First task is to the collect like terms that appear on the right side of the inequality.
         $-10y \leq -10$ Now we can use the addition property twice and get: $-10y \leq -10$
         $y \geq 1$ We now divide by –10 which means we have to change the direction of the inequality sign.

5.   Solve and graph: $3x < x + 4$ Use the addition property to subtract x from both sides, then divide by 2.
                  $x < 2$.

6.   Solve and graph: $5y + 7 > -11 - y$ Use the addition property to add y to each side and subtract 7 from each side.
                  $y > -3$ Then divide each side by 6.

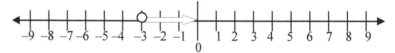

7.   Solve and graph: $2x + 6 \leq 5x$ Subtract $2x$ from each side and then divide by 3.
                  $2 \leq x$

We can restate this answer as $x \geq 2$, but either answer is correct since they both indicate that x is greater than or equal to 2.

8.   Solve and graph: $-6x + 2 \geq -2x + 18$ Use the addition property twice to move the variable term to the left (add
                  $x \leq -4$ $2x$) and the constant term to the right (subtract 2), then divide by –4
                        which means we have to reverse the sign of the inequality.

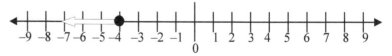

Lesson 3: Graphing

Earlier in this course we learned how to graph lines on the rectangular coordinate system. In this lesson we are going to expand our knowledge of graphing and learn about slopes, how to derive equations of lines given certain information, and how to determine if lines are parallel or perpendicular.

Graphing a Line Using Intercepts

First we will learn how to graph a line by finding the x and y intercepts of the line. The x intercept of a line is the point the line crosses the x-axis. Since any point that lies on the x-axis has a y value of 0, the ordered pair of the x intercept is $(x, 0)$. Similarly, the y intercept is the point the line crosses the y-axis and any point on the y-axis has an x value of 0. Hence, the ordered pair for the y intercept is $(0, y)$. Let's see how this information works in graphing a line.

Example 1. Graph: $2x + 3y = 6$

We will set up our table of x and y values as we normally do to determine values from which to graph a line, but this time we will only find the intercept points. We first substitute 0 for x and solve for y. Then reverse the process and substitute 0 for y and solve for x.

x	y	(x,y)
0	2	(0,2)
3	0	(3,0)

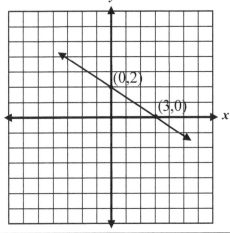

Now graph the line using these two points.

Slope

The slope of a line is an indication of how steep the line is, just as the slope of a hill is a measure of how steep it is. For a line, it is the measure of the change is the y values (called the rise) divided by the change in the x values (called the run). We put this in the form of an equation by selecting any two points on the line (x_1, y_1) and (x_2, y_2) and expressing the slope like this:

 A Rule to Remember! Slope $(m) = \dfrac{rise}{run} = \dfrac{y_2 - y_1}{x_2 - x_1}$ (We use the letter m to represent the slope)

Let's see how this works in a real example.

Example 2. Find the slope of the line containing these two points: (2,4) and (3,6)

To find the slope we substitute the values into the above equation. You should note that it doesn't matter which point you select for point #1 and which for point #2. For this example, we will select (2,4) as point #1 and (3,6) as point #2.

$$m = \frac{y_2 - y_1}{x_2 - x_1} = \frac{6-4}{3-2} = \frac{2}{1} = 2$$

9

Lesson 3: Graphing

Let's try another one, but this time we'll add some negative values.

Example 3. Find the slope of the line containing these two points: (2,-3) and (-4,-7)

$$m = \frac{-7-(-3)}{-4-2} = \frac{-7+3}{-4-2} = \frac{-4}{-6} = \frac{2}{3}$$

Determining the Slope of a Line from an Equation

You can tell a lot about a line simply by looking at the equation. One of the things you can determine is the slope of the line. To do this, we first need to understand the slope-intercept form of an equation.

A Rule to Remember!

Slope-intercept Form

$$y = mx + b$$

When an equation is in this form, the letter m, the coefficient of x, is the slope.

Example 4. What is the slope of this line? $y = 3x - 5$

Since this equation is in the slope-intercept form, the slope is represented by the coefficient of x, which is 3.

What happens if the equation is not in the slope-intercept form? You have to put it in that form before you can determine the slope.

Example 5. What is the slope of this line? $2x + 4y = 9$

To put this equation into the slope-intercept form, we must isolate y on the left by subtracting $2x$ from each side and then divide all terms by the coefficient of y.

$$\begin{array}{rl} 2x + 4y = 9 & \\ \underline{-2x \qquad -2x} & \text{Subtract } 2x \text{ from both sides.} \\ 4y = -2x + 9 & \end{array}$$

$$\frac{4y}{4} = \frac{-2x}{4} + \frac{9}{4} \qquad \text{Then divide all terms by 4.}$$

$$y = -\frac{1}{2}x + \frac{9}{4}$$

Now the equation is in the slope-intercept form so the slope is the coefficient of x, which is $-\frac{1}{2}$.

Determine the y Intercept from an Equation

When an equation is in the slope-intercept form, it is easy to substitute 0 for x. When we do that y equals b. Well, we said that the y intercept is defined as when the x value is 0, so b is the value of y in the ordered pair that represents the y intercept. In **Example 4**, b is -5 so the y intercept in this example is (0,-5). In **Example 5**, the y

intercept is $\left(0, \dfrac{9}{4}\right)$. You can see that writing an equation in the slope-intercept form is very helpful - we can determine the slope and y intercept simply by examining the equation and without making any calculations.

> **Example 6.** Find the slope and y intercept of: $-6x + 2y = 12$
>
> $y = 3x + 6$ Put this in the slope-intercept form.
>
> Therefore, the slope is 3 and the y intercept is (0,6).

Find the Equation of a Line Represented by a Given Point and Slope

We can use the slope-intercept form to help us find the equation of a line when all we know are the slope and a point that the line passes through. Here is how it works.

> **Example 7.** Find the equation of a line with a slope of 3 that passes through the point (5,2).

In the slope-intercept form of an equation, there are 4 unknowns (x, y, m, and b). In **Example 7**, we are told the values of 3 of them (x, y, and m). We substitute those three values in the slope-intercept form and solve for b.

$$y = mx + b$$
$$2 = 3(5) + b$$
$$2 = 15 + b$$
$$-13 = b$$

Now we take that value of b and the value of m (slope) and put them into the slope-intercept form and we have the equation that satisfies **Example 7**.

$$y = 3x - 13$$

> **Example 8.** Find the equation of a line with a slope of -2 that passes through the point (3,-4).
>
> $$y = mx + b$$
> $$-4 = -2(3) + b$$
> $$-4 = -6 + b$$
> $$2 = b$$

Substitute b and m into the slope-intercept form and we get: $y = -2x + 2$

Find the Equation of a Line Passing Through Two Given Points

Now we use our knowledge for finding the slope of a line containing two points and our knowledge gained in **Examples 7** and **8** to find the equation of a line that contains two given points.

> **Example 9.** Find the equation of a line passing through the points (3,-2) and (6,1).
>
> $$m = \frac{y_2 - y_1}{x_2 - x_1} = \frac{1 - (-2)}{6 - 3} = \frac{1 + 2}{3} = \frac{3}{3} = 1$$ First, use the slope formula to determine the slope.

$$y = mx + b$$
$$1 = 1(6) + b$$
$$-5 = b$$

$$y = x - 5$$

Then use the slope-intercept form to solve for b, by substituting the slope derived above and one of the points given in the example (either one is OK, but we will use the second point).

Now write the equation by substituting the m and b values into the slope-intercept form. (remember slope is 1.)

Determine Whether Lines are Parallel

 A Rule to Remember! Lines are parallel if they have the same slope. So, we determine if they are parallel by putting the equations in the slope intercept-form and comparing their slopes or m values. If the m values are exactly the same, the lines are parallel.

Example 10. Determine if these lines are parallel:
$$y = 3x + 5$$
$$y = 3x - 6$$

These equations are already in the slope-intercept form and the m value of each one is the same, so the lines are parallel.

Example 11. Determine if these lines are parallel:
$$3x + y = 15$$
$$2y = -6x + 8$$

Both of these equations need to be put in the slope-intercept form as follows,

First equation: $y = -3x + 15$
Second equation: $y = -3x + 4$

We can now tell the slopes are the same so the lines are parallel.

Determine Whether Lines are Perpendicular

 A Rule to Remember! Lines that are perpendicular also have a relationship between their slopes. But this relationship is a little more difficult to determine. For lines to be perpendicular, **the product of their slopes must equal -1.**

Example 12.   Determine if these lines are perpendicular:
$$y = -2x + 3$$
$$y = \frac{1}{2}x - 6$$

$$m_1 \bullet m_2 = -1$$
$$(-2)\left(\frac{1}{2}\right) = \frac{-2}{2} = -1$$

Since the product of their slopes does equal -1, the lines are perpendicular.

Remember, when asked to determine if lines are parallel or perpendicular, put the equations into the slope-intercept form and then look at their slopes. If they are the same, the lines are parallel, if their product is -1 they are perpendicular. If neither of these conditions exist the lines are neither parallel nor perpendicular.

Now you try.

Lesson 3: Graphing

Exercises

1. $3x + 4y = 12$ Graph by plotting the intercepts.

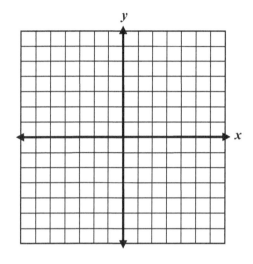

2. Determine the slope and y intercept of: $y = 4x + 5$

3. Determine the slope and y intercept of: $3x + 2y = -14$

4. Determine the slope of the line through these two points: (-2,3) and (3,-4)

5. Determine the slope of the line through these two points: (-1,-2) and (-4,-5)

6. Find the equation of the line with a slope of 5 passing through the point: (3,4)

7. Find the equation of the line that contains these two points: (4,-3) and (-2,-2)

8. Determine if these lines are parallel, perpendicular, or neither:

$$x + 2y = 10$$
$$4y = -2x - 5$$

9. Determine if these lines are parallel, perpendicular, or neither:

$$3y = -2x - 18$$
$$3x - 2y = -10$$

10. Determine if these lines are parallel, perpendicular, or neither:

$$y = -\frac{3}{2}x + 5$$
$$2y = 3x + 12$$

Lesson 3: Graphing

Solutions

1.   Graph by plotting the intercepts of: $3x + 4y = 12$

x	y	$(\ ,\ )$	
0	3	(0,3)	y-intercept
4	0	(4,0)	x-intercept

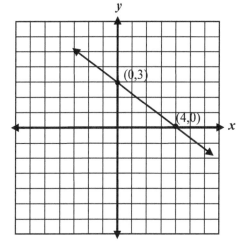

2.   Determine the slope and y intercept of: $y = 4x + 5$
This equation is already in the slope-intercept form, so the slope and y intercept can be read directly from the equation without any mathematical calculations.

$m = 4$ y intercept = (0,5)

3.   Determine the slope and y intercept of: $3x + 2y = -14$
This equation is not in the slope-intercept form, so we must do this first, by using the addition and multiplication properties and getting: $y = -\dfrac{3}{2}x - 7$

Now, we can determine the slope and y intercept: $m = -\dfrac{3}{2}$ y intercept = (0,-7)

4.   Determine the slope of the line through these two points: (-2,3) and (3,-4)
We have to use the formula for determining the slope (m).

$$m = \frac{y_2 - y_1}{x_2 - x_1} = \frac{-4 - 3}{3 - (-2)} = \frac{-7}{5}$$

5.   Determine the slope of the line through these two points: (-1,-2) and (-4,-5)
Use the formula for m: $m = \dfrac{-5 - (-2)}{-4 - (-1)} = \dfrac{-5 + 2}{-4 + 1} = \dfrac{-3}{-3} = 1$

6.   Find the equation of the line with a slope of 5 passing through the point: (3,4)
Substitute the values of m, x and y into the slope-intercept form to get:

$$y = mx + b$$
$$4 = 5(3) + b$$
$$4 = 15 + b$$
$$-11 = b$$

Now, substitute the m and b values into the slope-intercept form and get: $y = 5x - 11$

15

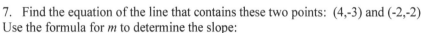

7. Find the equation of the line that contains these two points: (4,-3) and (-2,-2)
Use the formula for *m* to determine the slope:

$$m = \frac{y_2 - y_1}{x_2 - x_1} = \frac{-2 - (-3)}{-2 - 4} = \frac{-2 + 3}{-6} = -\frac{1}{6}$$

$$y = mx + b$$

Now substitute the *m* value and the *x* and *y* values from one of the given points into the slope-intercept form and solve for *b*.

$$-3 = -\frac{1}{6}(4) + b$$

$$-3 = -\frac{2}{3} + b$$

$$-\frac{7}{3} = b$$

$$y = mx + b$$

Now substitute the *m* and *b* values into the slope-intercept form to get the desired equation

$$y = -\frac{1}{6}x - \frac{7}{3}$$

8. Determine if these lines are parallel, perpendicular, or neither: $x + 2y = 10$

$$4y = -2x - 5$$

First equation: $y = -\frac{1}{2}x + 5$

Second equation: $y = -\frac{1}{2}x - \frac{5}{4}$

To answer this problem, we have to compare slopes and to do that we need to put the equations into the slope-intercept form. Comparing the values of *m* for each equation, we see that they are identical, so the answer is the lines are <u>parallel</u>.

9. Determine if these lines are parallel, perpendicular, or neither: $3y = -2x - 18$

$$3x - 2y = -10$$

First equation: $y = -\frac{2}{3}x - 6$

Second equation: $y = \frac{3}{2}x + 5$

To answer this problem, we have to compare slopes and to do that we need to put the equations into the slope-intercept form.

The *m* values are not the same so the lines are not parallel. The next test is to see if the product of the two slopes is equal to -1.

$$m_1 \bullet m_2 = \left(-\frac{2}{3}\right)\left(\frac{3}{2}\right) = -1$$

When the product of the slopes equals -1, then the lines are <u>perpendicular</u>.

10. Determine if these lines are parallel, perpendicular, or neither: $y = -\frac{3}{2}x + 5$

$$2y = 3x + 12$$

First equation: $y = -\frac{3}{2}x + 5$

Second equation: $y = \frac{3}{2}x + 6$

To answer this problem, we have to compare slopes and to do that we need to put the second equation into the slope-intercept form (the first is already in the that form.)

The slopes are not the same, one is negative and one is positive, so the lines are not parallel. The product of the two slopes is $-\frac{9}{4}$.

$$m_1 \bullet m_2 = \left(-\frac{3}{2}\right)\left(\frac{3}{2}\right) = -\frac{9}{4}$$

Since this product is not -1, the lines are <u>neither</u> parallel nor perpendicular.

Lesson 4: Rules for Exponents

In the lesson on exponential notation we learned how to write repeated multiplication in exponential notation. Then in the lesson about the multiplication property of exponents we learned some rules for multiplying terms with exponents. In this lesson we will review these rules and learn some more.

The Product Rule: $\qquad a^m \bullet a^n = a^{m+n}$ $\qquad$ Add the exponents

A Rule to Remember!

Example 1. $\qquad x^3 \bullet x^4 = x^{3+4} = x^7$

Example 2. $\qquad y^5 \bullet y^{10} = y^{5+10} = y^{15}$

The Quotient Rule: $\qquad \dfrac{a^m}{a^n} = a^{m-n}$ $\qquad$ Subtract the exponents

A Rule to Remember!

Example 3. $\qquad \dfrac{a^6}{a^2} = a^{6-2} = a^4$

Example 4. $\qquad \dfrac{x^9}{x^3} = x^{9-3} = x^6$

The Power Rule: $\qquad (a^m)^n = a^{mn}$ $\qquad$ Multiply the exponents

A Rule to Remember!

Example 5. $\qquad (z^3)^4 = z^{3 \bullet 4} = z^{12}$

Example 6. $\qquad (x^5)^7 = x^{5 \bullet 7} = x^{35}$

Raising a Product to a Power: $\qquad (ab)^n = a^n b^n$
Raise each factor to the indicated power

A Rule to Remember!

Example 7. $\qquad (3x)^2 = 3^2 \bullet x^2 = 9x^2$

Example 8. $\qquad (2x^2 y^3)^3 = 2^3 \bullet x^{2 \bullet 3} \bullet y^{3 \bullet 3} = 8x^6 y^9$

Negative Exponents: $a^{-n} = \dfrac{1}{a^n}$ **Terms are reciprocals of each other**

Example 9. $x^{-3}y^2 = \dfrac{y^2}{x^3}$

In mathematics, we generally write answers without negative exponents.

Example 10. $\dfrac{a^2 b^{-3}}{a^{-2} b^3 c^{-2}} = \dfrac{a^4 c^2}{b^6}$

Zero and One as Exponents: $a^1 = a$ **and** $a^0 = 1$

Example 11. $x^1 = x$

Example 12. $(y^2)^0 = 1$

Raising a Quotient to a Power: $\left(\dfrac{a}{b}\right)^n = \dfrac{a^n}{b^n}$

Raise the numerator and denominator to the indicated power

Example 13. $\left(\dfrac{2}{x}\right)^3 = \dfrac{2^3}{x^3} = \dfrac{8}{x^3}$

Example 14. $\left(\dfrac{x^3}{y^2}\right)^4 = \dfrac{x^{12}}{y^8}$

Now let's combine some of the rules in these examples:

Example 15. $\left(\dfrac{x^{-2}y^3}{x^3 y^{-4}}\right)^2 = \dfrac{x^{-4}y^6}{x^6 y^{-8}} = \dfrac{y^{14}}{x^{10}}$

Example 16. Evaluate: $x^{-2} + 16x^{-1} + x^0$ For $x = 2$

$$= \dfrac{1}{x^2} + \dfrac{16}{x} + x^0$$

$$= \dfrac{1}{(\ )^2} + \dfrac{1}{(\ )} + (\ )^0$$

$$= \dfrac{1}{(2)^2} + \dfrac{16}{2} + (2)^0 = \dfrac{1}{4} + 8 + 1 = 9\dfrac{1}{4}$$

Now it's your turn. ➤

Lesson 4: Rules for Exponents

Exercises

1. Simplify: $x^2 x^7$

2. Simplify: $(x^2)^7$

3. Simplify: $\dfrac{y^5}{y^3}$

4. Simplify: $\dfrac{a^5 b^7}{a^{-2} b^2 c}$

5. Simplify: $\left(\dfrac{x^{-4} y^{-5}}{x^2 y^2} \right)^2$

6. Simplify: $(-2x^2)^3$

7. Simplify: $(-3x^2 y^3)(-2x^3 y)$

8. Simplify: $(-2x^{-2} y^{-3} z^2)^2 (3x^{-1} yz)$

9. Simplify: 4^{-3}

10. Simplify: $\left(x^2 y^3 z^4 \right)^0$

11. Simplify: $3x^0$

12. Evaluate: $x^0 + x^{-1} + 32x^{-2}$ for $x = -4$

Lesson 4: Rules for Exponents

Solutions

1. Simplify: $x^2 x^7 = x^9$ Use the product rule and add exponents.

2. Simplify: $(x^2)^7 = x^{14}$ Use the power rule and multiply the exponents.

3. Simplify: $\dfrac{y^5}{y^3} = y^2$ Use the quotient rule and subtract the exponents.

4. Simplify: $\dfrac{a^5 b^7}{a^{-2} b^2 c} = \dfrac{a^7 b^5}{c}$ Use the rule for negative exponents to move the a^{-2} variable to the numerator, then use the product rule on the a terms and the quotient rule on the b terms.

5. Simplify: $\left(\dfrac{x^{-4} y^{-5}}{x^2 y^2}\right)^2 = \dfrac{x^{-8} y^{-10}}{x^4 y^4} = \dfrac{1}{x^{12} y^{14}}$ Use the power of a quotient rule, then the rule for negative exponents, and finally the product rule.

6. Simplify: $(-2x^2)^3 = (-2)^3 (x^2)^3 = -8x^6$ Raise each factor to the third power.

7. Simplify: $(-3x^2 y^3)(-2x^3 y) = 6x^5 y^4$ Use the product rule.

8. Simplify: $(-2x^{-2} y^{-3} z^2)^2 (3x^{-1} yz) = (4x^{-4} y^{-6} z^4)(3x^{-1} yz) = 12x^{-5} y^{-5} z^5 = \dfrac{12z^5}{x^5 y^5}$

   Be careful with the negative exponents.

9. Simplify: $4^{-3} = \dfrac{1}{64}$ Use the negative exponent rule.

10. Simplify: $\left(x^2 y^3 z^4\right)^0 = 1$ Anything raised to the zero power is 1.

11. Simplify: $3x^0 = 3 \bullet 1 = 3$ Only x is raised to the zero power.

12. Evaluate: $x^0 + x^{-1} + 32x^{-2}$ for $x = -4$

    $(-4)^0 + (-4)^{-1} + 32(-4)^{-2}$

    $1 - \dfrac{1}{4} + \dfrac{32}{16} = 2\dfrac{3}{4}$ Did you get this one?

20

Lesson 5: Scientific Notation

We have used exponential notation as a shorthand way to write some mathematical expressions. Now, we are going to use our knowledge of exponential notation to write very large and very small numbers in *scientific notation*. For example:

The distance from Earth to the Sun is 93,000,000 miles.
In scientific notation it is: 9.3×10^7 miles

The speed of light is 300,000,000 meters per second. In scientific notation it is: 3.0×10^8 mps
A very small number like 0.000000005 is written using scientific notation as: 5.0×10^{-9}

Notice that a very large number has a positive exponent and a very small number has a negative exponent. Now, the general rule for scientific notation:

Scientific Notation

A Rule to Remember!

Scientific notation for a number is an expression like this:

$$M \times 10^n \quad \text{Where } 1 \leq M < 10 \text{ and n is an integer}$$

This means that the number, M, must be equal to or greater than 1 and less than 10.

Let's try some conversions from decimal notation to scientific notation and then from scientific notation to decimal notation.

Example 1. **Convert 124,000,000 to scientific notation.**

Move the decimal point 8 places to the left and the result is: 1.24×10^8

Example 2. **Convert 9,562,000 to scientific notation.**

Move the decimal point 6 places to the left and the result is: 9.562×10^6

Example 3. **Convert 0.00478 to scientific notation.**

Move the decimal point 3 places to the right and the result is: 4.78×10^{-3}

Example 4. **Convert 0.0000008512 to scientific notation.**

Move the decimal point 7 places to the right and the result is: 8.512×10^{-7}

Example 5. **Convert from scientific notation to decimal notation:** 2.54×10^5

Move the decimal point 5 places to the right and the result is: 254,000

Example 6. **Convert from scientific notation to decimal notation:** 3.25×10^{-6}

Move the decimal point 6 places to the left: 0.00000325

Lesson 5: Scientific Notation

Multiplying Using Scientific Notation

We can use our knowledge of exponents to multiply numbers that are written in scientific notation. Consider these problems:

Example 7.   **Multiply:** $(2.4 \times 10^3)(1.3 \times 10^4)$

Remember that it doesn't matter what order we do the multiplication in so we can rewrite the problem as:
$$(2.4 \times 1.3)(10^3 \times 10^4)$$
$$3.12 \times 10^7$$

Example 8.   **Multiply:** $(4.8 \times 10^2)(5.2 \times 10^4)$

When we do the multiplication, we get:
$$24.96 \times 10^6$$

However, we are not finished with this problem yet because the answer is not in scientific notation because the number, M, is greater than 10. To put the answer in scientific notation, we have to move the decimal point one place to the left, in effect dividing by 10. We compensate for that by increasing the exponent by one, which is the same as multiplying by 10. The answer is: 2.496×10^7

One way to think about this is: For every decimal point you move to the left you have to increase the exponent by that same number. Now consider this example:

Example 9.   **Multiply:** $(3.5 \times 10^6)(5.7 \times 10^{-8})$

Our multiplication gives us this result:

$$19.95 \times 10^{-2}$$

Again, this is not in scientific notation. So, we move the decimal point one place to the left and increase the exponent by one and the result is:

$$1.995 \times 10^{-2+1}$$
$$1.995 \times 10^{-1}$$

Division Using Scientific Notation

We need our knowledge of exponents again to handle division problems using scientific notation. Consider these division problems:

Example 10.   **Divide** $(8.4 \times 10^6) \div (2.5 \times 10^4)$ Let's start by rewriting the problem.

$$\frac{(8.4 \times 10^6)}{(2.5 \times 10^4)}$$

$$= \frac{8.4}{2.5} \times \frac{10^6}{10^4} \qquad \text{Then further rewrite it.}$$

$$= 3.36 \times 10^2 \qquad \text{Then dividing (remembering to subtract exponents)}$$

Example 11.   **Divide:** $\dfrac{(4.6\times10^6)}{(9.2\times10^2)}$

$$= 0.5\times10^4$$

This is not in scientific notation, so we have to move the decimal point one place to the right this time which means we have to <u>decrease</u> the exponent by one.   It looks like this:

$$= 5.0\times10^{4-1}$$
$$= 5.0\times10^3$$

Example 12.   **Divide:** $\dfrac{(2.16\times10^{-5})}{(4.5\times10^6)}$

$$= 0.48\times10^{-5-6}$$
$$= 0.48\times10^{-11}$$
$$= 4.8\times10^{-11-1}$$
$$= 4.8\times10^{-12}$$

Now it's your turn.

23

Lesson 5: Scientific Notation

Lesson 5: Scientific Notation

Exercises

1.   Convert 125,000 to scientific notation

2.   Convert 0.0000000526 to scientific notation

3.   Convert 3.287×10^6 from scientific notation to decimal notation

4.   Convert 9.684×10^{-4} from scientific notation to decimal notation

5.   Multiply and write answer in scientific notation: $(2.24 \times 10^3)(3.6 \times 10^2)$

6.   Multiply and write answer in scientific notation: $(8.26 \times 10^{-2})(6.1 \times 10^7)$

7.   Multiply and write answer in scientific notation: $(5.25 \times 10^{-3})(3.5 \times 10^{-5})$

8.   Divide and write answer in scientific notation: $(4.2 \times 10^3) \div (8.4 \times 10^5)$

9.   Divide and write answer in scientific notation: $\dfrac{(2.1 \times 10^6)}{(5.25 \times 10^{-3})}$

10.   Divide and write answer in scientific notation: $\dfrac{(1.6 \times 10^{-5})}{(6.4 \times 10^{-8})}$

Lesson 5: Scientific Notation

Solutions

1.   Convert 125,000 to scientific notation: 1.25×10^5

2.   Convert 0.0000000526 to scientific notation: 5.26×10^{-8}

3.   Convert 3.287×10^6 from scientific notation to decimal notation: 3,287,000

4.   Convert 9.684×10^{-4} from scientific notation to decimal notation: 0.0009684

5.   Multiply and write answer in scientific notation: $(2.24 \times 10^3)(3.6 \times 10^2)$
     $= 8.064 \times 10^5$ Remember to add the exponents

6.   Multiply and write answer in scientific notation: $(8.26 \times 10^{-2})(6.1 \times 10^7)$
     $= 50.386 \times 10^5$ This is not yet in scientific notation.
     $= 5.0386 \times 10^6$

7.   Multiply and write answer in scientific notation: $(5.25 \times 10^{-3})(3.5 \times 10^{-5})$
     $= 18.375 \times 10^{-8}$
     $= 1.8375 \times 10^{-7}$ Add 1 to the exponent of –8 and you get –7.

8.   Divide and write answer in scientific notation: $(4.2 \times 10^3) \div (8.4 \times 10^5)$
     $= 0.5 \times 10^{-2}$ This is not in scientific notation
     $= 5.0 \times 10^{-3}$ Subtract 1 from the exponent of –2 to get –3

9.   Divide and write answer in scientific notation: $\dfrac{(2.1 \times 10^6)}{(5.25 \times 10^{-3})}$
     $= 0.4 \times 10^{6-(-3)}$ Be careful with this combination of exponents.
     $= 0.4 \times 10^9$
     $= 4.0 \times 10^8$ Subtract 1 from the exponent of 9 to get 8.

10. Divide and write answer in scientific notation: $\dfrac{(1.6 \times 10^{-5})}{(6.4 \times 10^{-8})}$
     $= 0.25 \times 10^{-5-(-8)}$
     $= 0.25 \times 10^3$
     $= 2.5 \times 10^2$

Lesson 6: Special Products of Binomials

This lesson will look at some special products of binomials. In the next lesson we start to learn how to factor. That means we will look at an expression and try to find factors of that expression. The more familiar you are with the result you get when you multiply certain binomials together, the easier factoring will be.

The first special product we will examine will be the sum and difference of two terms. Let's look at two terms, x and 4, and take the product of their sum and difference.

Example 1. $(x+4)(x-4)$

If we FOIL this, we get: $x^2 - 4x + 4x - 16$

After we combine like terms, we get: $x^2 - 16$

Notice that the middle terms canceled each other out, that is, their sum is zero. Let's look at one more example to see if the same pattern exists. Look at the product of the sum and difference of the two terms $3y$ and 7:

Example 2. $(3y+7)(3y-7)$

If we FOIL this, we get: $9y^2 - 21y + 21y - 49$

After we combine like terms, we get: $9y^2 - 49$

Again the middle terms cancel out. From this we adopt the general rule for the product of the sum and difference of two terms, which is:

The Rule for the Product of the Sum and Difference of the Same Two Terms	A Rule to Remember!
$$(A+B)(A-B) = A^2 - B^2$$	

This means that whenever we have the product of the sum and difference of the same two terms, we can save ourselves the time of using FOIL and simply write the answer as the first term squared minus the second term squared. Here are a few more examples:

Example 3. $(x-8)(x+8)$

$= x^2 - 8^2$ ⟵ First term squared minus the second term squared

$= x^2 - 64$

Example 4. $(4x+3z)(4x-3z)$

$= (4x)^2 - (3z)^2$ ⟵ First term squared minus the second term squared

$= 16x^2 - 9z^2$

Next let's look at squaring binomials.

Example 5. $(x+5)^2$

Remember that this means: $(x+5)(x+5)$

If we FOIL this, we get: $x^2 + 5x + 5x + 25$

After we combine like terms, we get: $x^2 + 10x + 25$

This time we didn't eliminate any terms, but the middle terms were exactly the same. So let's look at another example and see if it works the same.

Lesson 6: Special Products of Binomials

Example 6. $(y+4)^2$

Again, we will use FOIL on this product: $(y+4)(y+4)$

We get: $y^2 + 4y + 4y + 16$

After we combine like terms, we get: $y^2 + 8y + 16$

Like **Example 5**, this example had two identical middle terms. From this, we generate the rule for squaring a binomial:

The Rule for Squaring a Binomial

A Rule to Remember!

$$(A+B)^2 = A^2 + 2AB + B^2$$

This rule means that whenever you have a binomial squared, you can avoid using FOIL and write the answer as the square of the first term plus twice the product of the two terms plus the second term squared. Here are a few more examples.

Example 7. $(z+3)^2$
$$= z^2 + 6z + 9$$

Example 8. $(3x+4)^2$
$$= 9x^2 + 24x + 16$$

In our examples of binomial squares, we have used only positive terms. Let's look at the difference of two terms.

Example 9. $(x-5)^2$

First write it like this: $(x-5)(x-5)$

Then use FOIL: $x^2 - 5x - 5x + 25$

Notice that in **Example 9** the middle two terms are the same, but this time they are negative terms. When we combine them, we get: $x^2 - 10x + 25$

We can now add to the rule for squaring a binomial:

Complete Rule for the Squaring of Binomials

A Rule to Remember!

$$(A+B)^2 = A^2 + 2AB + B^2$$

$$(A-B)^2 = A^2 - 2AB + B^2$$

Note that the only difference is the sign of the middle term. Here are some examples using the square of the difference of two terms.

Example 10. $(y-6)^2$
$$= y^2 - 12y + 36$$

Lesson 6: Special Products of Binomials

Example 11. $(2z-7)^2$

$$= 4z^2 - 28z + 49$$

Practice these a lot, because it will really make factoring easier if you can recognize these patterns. Remember, factoring is the opposite of multiplying. With factoring, you try to look at an expression, and figure out what two (or more) terms could be multiplied together to get that result. The next few lessons will get into factoring.

Before we do those, try these problems.

Lesson 6: Special Products of Binomials

Lesson 6: Special Products of Binomials

Exercises

1. $(x-1)(x+1)$

2. $(2y+5)(2y-5)$

3. $(3z-6)(3z+6)$

4. $(4a+3b)(4a-3b)$

5. $(x+3)^2$

6. $(2y+5)^2$

7. $(5z+1)^2$

8. $(x-9)^2$

9. $(2y-6)^2$

10. $(5a-3b)^2$

Lesson 6: Special Products of Binomials

Solutions

1. $(x-1)(x+1)$ Answer: $x^2 - 1$

This is the product of the sum and difference of the same terms (middle terms cancel).

2. $(2y+5)(2y-5)$ Answer: $4y^2 - 25$

Same type of problem as #1.

3. $(3z-6)(3z+6)$ Answer: $9z^2 - 36$

Also the product of the sum and difference of the same terms.

4. $(4a+3b)(4a-3b)$ Answer: $16a^2 - 9b^2$

Same as the previous three problems. This has two variables, but the process is the same.

5. $(x+3)^2$ Answer: $x^2 + 6x + 9$

This is a binomial squared. Write it as two binomials and FOIL it until you get used to the process.

6. $(2y+5)^2$ Answer: $4y^2 + 20y + 25$

Remember, a binomial square is of the form: $(A+B)^2 = A^2 + 2AB + B^2$

7. $(5z+1)^2$ Answer: $25z^2 + 10z + 1$

Another binomial square.

8. $(x-9)^2$ Answer: $x^2 - 18x + 81$

This is also a binomial square, like the last three problems. The only difference this time is the sign.

9. $(2y-6)^2$ Answer: $4y^2 - 24y + 36$

Same as problem #8.

10. $(5a-3b)^2$ Answer: $25a^2 - 30ab + 9b^2$

Another binomial square with a negative sign.

Lesson 7: Introduction to Factoring

You should recall that when we multiply two numbers together to get a product, the two numbers are called factors. The process of factoring is just the opposite. Factoring is starting with the product and developing the numbers that when multiplied together give you the product. For example, if we multiply 5 times 3 we get 15. The numbers 5 and 3 are <u>factors</u> of the product 15. Here are some other examples of factoring:

Example 1.   Find factors of $2x$

The factors for $2x$ are 2 and x. If we multiply 2 times x we get $2x$.

Example 2.   Find factors of $12x^2$

There are many factors of this term, but two factors are $3x$ and $4x$. We can verify that these are factors by multiplying $3x$ times $4x$ the result is $12x^2$, which is the term we started with.

Now we are going to factor polynomials with more than one term. We will begin with a binomial and try to find factors of that. Remember our distributive property?

$$a(b+c) = ab + ac$$

Well, with factoring, we are starting with $ab + ac$ and trying to get to $a(b+c)$ or, in other words, by what can we divide both terms. Look at these examples:

Example 3.   Factor: $2x + 8$

When we say to factor an expression, it means we want to find its factors. Here we want to know what the common factor is in each term and that is 2 (each term can be divided by 2). So we can factor $2x + 8$ as:
$$2(x+4)$$

When we factor an expression, the first thing to do is to look for common factors in each term – and we want to look for the ***largest*** common factor. Now let's look for common factors in a trinomial.

Example 4.   Factor: $3x^3 + 9x^2 + 12x$

In this polynomial, the largest common factor is $3x$. So when we factor this expression we would get:

$$3x(x^2 + 3x + 4)$$

 You can always check your answer when factoring, by multiplying the factors to see if you get the original expression.

Factoring Trinomials of the Type: $x^2 + bx + c$

Next, we will look at factoring a trinomial of the type: $x^2 + bx + c$. The important characteristic of this type is that the coefficient of x^2 is one. Remember in the last section how we used FOIL? Well, now we will use FOIL in reverse. We start with the trinomial and try to find the two binomial factors. Start with this example:

Example 5.   Factor: $x^2 + 6x + 8$

We know from the FOIL process that the first term of this trinomial is the product of the first terms of each of the binomials and our only option here is x times x. So, we have this much known so far:

$$(x +\quad)(x +\quad)$$

The hard part of this type of problem is determining the last terms of the binomials. The process is to find two numbers that multiplied together give you the last term in the trinomial and the sum of which give you the middle term. We find this by looking at all the possible factors of the third term, 8, and finding the sum of those factors. We want the sum to equal the coefficient of the middle term. Here is the process:

Factors	Sum
8 and 1	9
4 and 2	**6** ←

Since the factors 4 and 2 when added together give the coefficient we are looking for, we can use these numbers as the second terms in the binomials, which yields the factors:

$$(x + 4)(x + 2)$$

We can check our answer by using FOIL. The result is: $x^2 + 6x + 8$ which is our original expression, so our answer checks. Now let's try a few more.

Example 6.   Factor: $x^2 - 11x + 24$

Note that in this example, the sign of the second term is negative. The only way we can have the second term negative and the third term positive is for the sign of the second term of each binomial to be negative. We, therefore, will look for factors of 24 such that the sum of the factors is 11.

Factors	Sum
24 and 1	25
12 and 2	14
8 and **3**	**11** ←
6 and 4	10

The pair of factors we are looking for is 8 and 3. So, our factors are: $(x - 8)(x - 3)$

Again, checking our answer by using FOIL we find the above product is: $x^2 - 11x + 24$ so our answer is correct.

In **Examples 5** and **Example 6**, the sign of the third term was positive. Now, let's look at trinomials that have the third term negative. In this case, the only way to have the third term negative is to have the signs in the binomials to be different. Look at these examples.

Example 7. $x^2 + x - 30$

The negative third term should be a red flag alert that tells you that you need to look at factors of the third term such that the <u>difference</u> of the factors yields the middle term coefficient.

Lesson 7: Introduction to Factoring

Factors	Difference
30 and 1	29
15 and 2	13
10 and 3	7
6 and **5**	**1** ←

In this case, the factors 6 and 5 yield the correct middle term coefficient. Since the signs of the factors are different, we have to decide which sign goes with which number. Since the sign of the middle term is positive, we want the larger number to have the positive sign. So, our factors are:

$$(x+6)(x-5)$$

We check our answer by FOILing and the result is: $x^2 + x - 30$

Example 8. $\quad x^2 - x - 30$

Notice that this example is not much different than **Example 7**. The only difference is that the middle term is negative. We have the same factors of the third term, but this time we want the larger number to have the negative sign. This results in the factors of:

$$(x-6)(x+5)$$

FOILing this we get the product: $x^2 - x - 30$ so our answer is correct.

We have done four examples with the arrangement of the signs different in each case. You should remember that if the sign of the third term is positive, you will look for the sum of the factors. But if the sign of the third term is negative, you will look for the difference of the factors. We can summarize that as follows:

Example 9. $\quad x^2 + bx + c = (x + \ )(x + \ )$

Example 10. $\quad x^2 - bx + c = (x - \ )(x - \ )$

Example 11. $\quad x^2 + bx - c = (x + \ )(x - \ ) \qquad$ The larger factor gets the + sign.

Example 12. $\quad x^2 - bx - c = (x + \ )(x - \ ) \qquad$ The larger factor gets the − sign.

Here are a few more examples illustrating the relationship of the signs:

Example 13. $\quad x^2 + 10x + 24 = (x+6)(x+4)$

Example 14. $\quad x^2 - 13x + 42 = (x-6)(x-7)$

Example 15. $\quad y^2 + 2y - 15 = (y+5)(y-3)$

Example 16. $\quad a^2 - 5a - 24 = (a-8)(a+3)$

When factoring, your first step should ALWAYS be to look for common factors. Then, look at the result to see if further factoring is possible. Consider **Example 17.**

35

Example 17. $2x^2 + 24x + 64$

You should look to see if any common factor exists in all three terms. In this case, there is a common factor of 2. Factoring out the 2, we get:

$$2(x^2 + 12x + 32)$$

Now we look at the trinomial in the parentheses to see if that can be factored and we find it can:

$$2(x+4)(x+8)$$

We can check the result by reversing the process we just did. FOIL the two binomials and then multiply by 2, and we find the answer does check.

Now it's your turn

Lesson 7: Introduction to Factoring

Exercises

1. $4x + 16$

2. $2x^2 + 18x$

3. $3y^2 + 6y + 12$

4. $4z^3 - 24z^2 - 12z$

5. $x^2 + 8x + 12$

6. $z^2 - 12z + 20$

7. $a^2 + 5a - 14$

8. $y^2 - y - 56$

9. $2x^2 - 6x - 36$

10. $3y^2 + 33y + 72$

Lesson 7: Introduction to Factoring

Solutions

1. $4x + 16 = 4(x + 4)$ The common factor in this problem is 4.

2. $2x^2 + 18x = 2x(x + 9)$ The common factor in this problem is $2x$.

3. $3y^2 + 6y + 12 = 3(y^2 + 2y + 4)$ The common factor is 3.

4. $4z^3 - 24z^2 - 12z = 4z(z^2 - 6z - 3)$ The common factor is $4z$.

5. $x^2 + 8x + 12 = (x + 6)(x + 2)$

    The factors we want are the ones that when multiplied together equal 12 (the last term), but when added together equal 8 (the coefficient of the middle term).

Factors	Sum
12 and 1	13
6 and **2**	**8** ←
4 and 3	7

6. $z^2 - 12z + 20 = (z - 10)(z - 2)$

    The factors we want here are 10 and 2, since their product is 20 (the last term) and their sum is 12 (the middle term). Note that the signs of both are negative in order to give us a negative middle term but a positive last term.

Factors	Sum
20 and 1	21
10 and **2**	**12** ←
5 and 4	9

7. $a^2 + 5a - 14 = (a + 7)(a - 2)$

    In this problem, we are looking for factors of 14 such that their **difference** is 5. We do this because the sign of the third term is negative. The factors are 7 and 2. The factor 7 gets the positive sign and the 2 gets the negative sign because we want a middle term that is positive.

Factors	Difference
14 and 1	13
7 and 2	**5** ←

8. $y^2 - y - 56 = (y - 8)(y + 7)$

    Again, because the sign of the third term is negative, we want to look at the **difference** of factors of 56. In this case, the factors are 8 and 7, since their difference is 1. The larger of the two factors gets the negative sign, the other gets the positive sign.

Factors	Difference
56 and 1	55
28 and 2	26
14 and 4	10
8 and **7**	**1** ←

9. $2x^2 - 6x - 36 = 2(x^2 - 3x - 18)$
    $$= 2(x - 6)(x + 3)$$

    Remember the first step in factoring is always to look for a common factor. After factoring out the common factor look at the remaining expression to see if it can be factored. In this problem, after factoring out the common factor of 2, we can further factor the trinomial into two binomials using 6 and 3 as the factors, with the 6 getting the negative sign and 3 getting the positive sign.

Factors	Difference
18 and 1	17
9 and 2	7
6 and 3	3 ←

10. $3y^2 + 33y + 72 = 3(y^2 + 11y + 24)$
    $$= 3(y + 8)(y + 3)$$

    The common factor in this problem is 3. The remaining trinomial can be factored into two binomials using the factors of 8 and 3.

Factors	Sum
24 and 1	25
12 and 2	14
8 and 3	**11** ←
6 and 4	10

Lesson 8: Factoring Squares

In the lesson "Special Products of Binomials", we looked at some patterns in the multiplication of binomials. We mentioned that these patterns would be good to remember because it would help in factoring. Well, here we are! First let's repeat the special products:

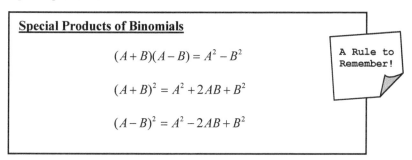

Special Products of Binomials

$$(A+B)(A-B) = A^2 - B^2$$

$$(A+B)^2 = A^2 + 2AB + B^2$$

$$(A-B)^2 = A^2 - 2AB + B^2$$

A Rule to Remember!

Now, we will work in the reverse order. The first of the special products results in the <u>difference</u> of two squares, A^2 and B^2. So, we will look for that pattern, the difference of squares, and then show the factors as the sum and difference of the two perfect square factors. Here's two examples of how it works.

Example 1.   Factor: $x^2 - 25$

Since x^2 and 25 are perfect squares of x and 5, we can write the factors of **Example 1** as:

$$(x-5)(x+5)$$

We can check to see if we have the correct answer by FOILing the binomials, which results in:

$$x^2 + 5x - 5x - 25$$
$$= x^2 - 25$$ The answer checks.

Example 2.   Factor: $4y^2 - 49$

Even though the first term has a coefficient, this problem still is the difference of squares. The factors in this problem are the sum and difference of 2y and 7, and the answer is:

$$(2y+7)(2y-7)$$

Checking the answer, we get: $4y^2 - 14y + 14y - 49$
$$4y^2 - 49$$ The answer checks.

Here are two more examples of the difference of squares:

Example 3.   Factor: $9 - 16b^2$

Even though this may look a little different, it is still the difference of squares because $9 = 3^2$ and $16b^2 = (4b)^2$. So, the factors are:

$$(3-4b)(3+4b)$$

Lesson 8: Factoring Squares

Example 4.   Factor: $25x^2 - 64y^2$

This may look even stranger than the last example, but it still is the difference of squares and the factors are:

$$(5x - 8y)(5x + 8y)$$

Now let's look at factoring trinomial squares. A trinomial square results from squaring a binomial. Look at the last two problems in the box on the first page of this section. These are examples of trinomial squares. It's a little more difficult to recognize trinomial squares than it is to recognize the difference of squares, so we have a few guidelines to help you.

A Rule to Remember!

Guidelines for Recognizing Trinomial Squares

In order for an expression to be a trinomial square like:
$$A^2 + 2AB + B^2 \quad \text{or} \quad A^2 - 2AB + B^2$$

- the two terms, A^2 and B^2, must be squares,
- there must be no negative sign before A^2 and B^2, and
- if you multiply A and B, and then double it, you should get the middle term.

Let's try some examples.

Example 5.   Factor: $x^2 + 8x + 16$

The A^2 and B^2 terms in this problem are x^2 and 16 and both are squares (x and 4). Neither A^2 nor B^2 are negative, and twice the product of A and B (twice the product of x and 4) is equal to the middle term. So, this is a trinomial square and the factors are:

$$(x + 4)^2$$

We can check the answer by FOILing and we get:

$$(x+4)(x+4) = x^2 + 4x + 4x + 16$$
$$= x^2 + 8x + 16 \qquad \text{The answer checks.} \quad$$

Example 6.   Factor: $y^2 - 14y + 49$

This meets the three guidelines in that the first and third terms are squares (of y and 7) and they are positive, and the middle term is twice the product of y and 7. The factors, therefore, are:
$$(y - 7)^2$$

Example 7.   Factor: $4x^2 + 12xy + 9y^2$

This meets the guidelines even though it looks a little different. The first and third term squares are $(2x)^2$ and $(3y)^2$, which are both positive and twice the product of these two squares is equal to the middle term. So, the factors are:
$$(2x + 3y)^2$$

Lesson 8: Factoring Squares

Example 8.   Factor: $2x^2 + 12x + 18$

This does <u>not</u> meet the guidelines for a trinomial square – at least as it is now. But remember that the first step in factoring is always to look to see if there is a common factor in all the terms. In this case, there is a common factor of 2. The problem now becomes:

$$2(x^2 + 6x + 9)$$

Now the expression in parentheses does meet the guidelines for a trinomial square and the complete answer to **Example 8** is:

$$2(x + 3)^2$$

When asked to factor a problem, you should follow this process:

Factoring Process

    A Rule to Remember!

- Look for a common factor

- Factor completely

- Check your answer by multiplying

Here is an example of a problem that many times does not get factored completely.

Example 9.   Factor: $x^4 - 1$

You should recognize that this is the difference of squares and the factors are:

$$(x^2 - 1)(x^2 + 1)$$

Our factoring process says to factor completely, so we should always look to see if any of the resulting factors can be factored again. In this case, the first factor $(x^2 - 1)$ is still the difference of squares so we can write the factors of **Example 9** as:

$$(x + 1)(x - 1)(x^2 + 1)$$

Why don't we factor $(x^2 + 1)$? Because the <u>sum</u> of squares cannot be factored!

Here are two more examples of this type:

Example 10.   Factor: $y^4 - 16$

Result of factoring first time: $(y^2 - 4)(y^2 + 4)$

Complete factoring: $(y + 2)(y - 2)(y^2 + 4)$

Lesson 8: Factoring Squares

Example 11.   Factor: $32x^4 - 162$

Factor out the common factor: $2(16x^4 - 81)$

Interim result: $2(4x^2 - 9)(4x^2 + 9)$

Complete factoring: $2(2x + 3)(2x - 3)(4x^2 + 9)$

Now it's your turn ➡

Lesson 8: Factoring Squares

Exercises

1. $y^2 - 25$

2. $16a^2 - 49b^2$

3. $4x^2 + 9$

4. $x^2 + 18x + 81$

5. $3y^2 - 48y + 192$

6. $4a^2 + 20ab + 25b^2$

7. $x^4 + 6x^2 + 9$

8. $t^4 - 16$

9. $81x^4 - 16$

10. $32x^4 - 2$

Lesson 8: Factoring Squares

Solutions

1. $y^2 - 25 = (y-5)(y+5)$

This is the difference of two squares.

2. $16a^2 - 49b^2 = (4a-7b)(4a+7b)$

This is also the difference of two squares, but the first term had a coefficient.

3. $4x^2 + 9$ Can't be factored.

The sum of squares can't be factored.

4. $x^2 + 18x + 81 = (x+9)^2$

This is a trinomial square.

5. $3y^2 - 48y + 192 = 3(y^2 - 16y + 64) = 3(y-8)^2$

This is also a trinomial square after factoring out the common factor of 3.

6. $4a^2 + 20ab + 25b^2 = (2a+5b)^2$

This is a trinomial square, but it may have been a little harder because the first term had a coefficient and there were two variables. However, if you always check your answer, you will see that this is correct.

7. $x^4 + 6x^2 + 9 = (x^2+3)^2$

Did you have trouble with this one?   It is a trinomial square since it meets all the guidelines, but the higher exponent may have caused you problems.

8. $t^4 - 16 = (t+2)(t-2)(t^2+4)$

Did you remember to factor completely?

9. $81x^4 - 16 = (3x-2)(3x+2)(9x^2+4)$

This one also required you to factor twice.

10. $32x^4 - 2 = 2(2x-1)(2x+1)(4x^2+1)$

After factoring out 2, we are left with a difference of squares that can be factored twice.

Lesson 9: Factoring Using Grouping

So far in our discussion of factoring, we have factored binomials and trinomials. The next step is to look at some polynomials with four terms and see how to factor them. To begin our understanding of factoring by grouping, consider this expression.

Example 1. Factor: $x^2(x) + 2(x)$

It's pretty apparent, from the way this is written, that the common factor is x and this could be factored as:

$$x(x^2 + 2)$$

Now, let's look at a slightly different problem. This one also has a common factor and, from the way it is written, you should easily spot that factor:

Example 2. Factor: $x^2(x+1) + 2(x+1)$

The common factor is $(x+1)$, so the factors of this problem are:

$$(x^2 + 2)(x+1)$$

Now, let's look at a four term polynomial and see if we can use the concept of grouping to factor it.

Example 3. Factor: $x^3 + 2x^2 + 3x + 6$

The first thing we do is look for a common factor in each of the four terms and there is none. But there is a common factor in the first two terms (x^2) and a different common factor in the last two terms (3). Here's what happens when we use that information:

$$x^2(x+2) + 3(x+2)$$

Now it looks like the **Example 2**, and we should recognize that the common factor is $(x+2)$. So the correct factors of **Example 3** are:

$$(x^2 + 3)(x+2) \qquad \text{Use FOIL to show that these are the correct factors.}$$

Here is another example of factoring by grouping.

Example 4. Factor: $x^3 - 6x^2 + 2x - 12$

There are no common factors in all four terms so we look for a common factor in the first two terms and that is x^2 and the common factor for the last two terms is 2. So far, we have:

$$x^2(x-6) + 2(x-6)$$

Now our common factor is $(x-6)$ and the factors of **Example 4** are:

$$(x^2 + 2)(x-6)$$

Lesson 9: Factoring Using Grouping

Here's another example.

Example 5.   Factor: $6x^3 - 8x^2 + 9x - 12$

The common factor in the first two terms is $2x^2$ and 3 in the last two terms. So, it looks like this:

$$2x^2(3x - 4) + 3(3x - 4)$$

The common factor is now $(3x - 4)$ and the factors of **Example 5** are:

$$(2x^2 + 3)(3x - 4)$$

Now, let's try one more example of this type of grouping problem, one that frequently causes errors with signs.

Example 6.   Factor: $12y^3 + 9y^2 - 8y - 6$

The common factor for the first two terms $3y^2$ and let's try 2 for the last two terms.

$$3y^2(4y + 3) + 2(-4y - 3)$$

Written this way we don't have an apparent common factor, but if we factor out a –2 instead of 2, here's what we get:

$$3y^2(4y + 3) - 2(4y + 3)$$

Now we do have a common factor and we would write our answer as:

$$(3y^2 - 2)(4y + 3)$$

Our next task is to use the grouping method on some trinomials. Previously, we had trinomials of the type: $x^2 + bx + c$. With this type of polynomial we looked for factors of c, such that the sum (or difference) would give us the middle term. Now, we will look at trinomials of the type: $ax^2 + bx + c$. There are some different approaches to this type of problem, but the method discussed here will be the grouping method. Here are the steps to follow for factoring a trinomial where the leading coefficient is an integer greater than one.

Steps for Factoring $ax^2 + bx + c$ Using Grouping	A Rule to Remember!
Step 1: Factor out a common factor, if one exists.	
Step 2: Multiply a times c.	
Step 3: Factor ac so that the sum of the factors (if sign of c is positive) or the difference of the factors (if sign of c is negative) is b.	
Step 4: Split the middle term using the factors found in step 3	
Step 5: Factor by grouping	

Lesson 9: Factoring Using Grouping

This probably sounds pretty confusing, so let's try some examples.

Example 7. Factor: $3x^2 + 14x + 15$

There are no common factors, so we multiply 3 times 15 to get 45. We then look for factors of 45 such that the sum (since the sign of the third term is positive) is 14. To do that, you ought to set up a table like this:

Factors	Sum
45 and 1	46
15 and 3	18
9 and 5	**14** ⬅

The factors that we want are 9 and 5. Now we split the middle term using these factors like this:

$$3x^2 + 9x + 5x + 15$$

Note that the two middle terms, when combined, equal the original middle term of $14x$.

Now, we factor by grouping. The common factor of the first two terms is $3x$ and 5 in the last two terms. So, we have:

$$3x(x+3) + 5(x+3)$$

And the factors for **Example 7** are: $(3x+5)(x+3)$

Example 8. Factor: $6x^2 + 31x + 18$

Since there are no common factors, we find the product of 6 and 18 which is 108. Then we build our table:

Factors	Sum
108 and 1	109
54 and 2	56
36 and 3	39
27 and 4	**31** ⬅
18 and 6	24
12 and 9	21

The factors we want are 27 and 4 since they add to 31 which is the coefficient of the middle term. Now, we split the middle term using these factors as follows:

$$6x^2 + 27x + 4x + 18$$

Note, that we could have written the middle terms in the opposite order $(+4x + 27x)$ and we would still get the correct answer. It doesn't matter what the order is – just that they algebraically combine to equal the middle term of the original expression.

Next, we factor by grouping:

$$3x(2x+9) + 2(2x+9)$$
$$= (3x+2)(2x+9)$$

Lesson 9: Factoring Using Grouping

Now let's try an example that has a negative c term.   We will have to look at the difference of factors in this case.

Example 9.   Factor: $9y^2 - 18y - 16$

Since there are no common factors, we multiply 9 times 16 and get 144 and then we set up our table.

Factors	Difference
144 and 1	143
72 and 2	70
48 and 3	45
36 and 4	32
24 and **6**	**18** ←
18 and 8	10
16 and 9	7
12 and 12	0

 Note: It isn't necessary to list all the possible factors – only list the factors until you find the correct ones. In this case we could have stopped after finding 24 and 6.

$$\overset{\displaystyle -18y}{9y^2 - 24y + 6y - 16}$$ We combine the factors 24y and 6y so that the middle term is $-18y$.

$$3y(3y-8) + 2(3y-8)$$ Then we factor by grouping.
$$= (3y+2)(3y-8)$$

Let's try one more before you get your turn.

Example 10.   Factor: $18z^2 + 24z - 10$

Remember the first step in all factoring problems is to look for common factors in all terms and we have a common factor of 2 in this example. Now the problem is:

$$2(9z^2 + 12z - 5)$$

Now find the product of 9 and 5 which is 45. Then set up the table looking for the difference of the factors that equal 12.

Factors	Difference
45 and 1	44
15 and **3**	**12** ←
9 and 5	4

Next we split the middle term and factor by grouping:

$$2(9z^2 + 15z - 3z - 5)$$
$$= 2[3z(3z+5) - 1(3z+5)]$$
$$= 2(3z-1)(3z+5)$$

OK, now it's your turn

Lesson 9: Factoring Using Grouping

Exercises

1. $y^2(y+5)-3(y+5)$

2. $3x^3+x^2-9x-3$

3. $x^3+4x^2+5x+20$

4. $12a^3+28a^2-15a-35$

5. $6x^2-x-15$

6. $12x^2-25x+12$

7. $6x^2+11x-10$

8. $10x^2-31x-14$

9. $6x^3+8x^2+2x$

10. $8x^2+4x-60$

Lesson 9: Factoring Using Grouping

Solutions

1. $y^2(y+5)-3(y+5) = (y^2-3)(y+5)$ The common factor is $(y+5)$

2. $3x^3+x^2-9x-3 = (x^2-3)(3x+1)$ The common factor in the first two terms is x^2 and the common factor in the last two terms is –3. Your interim answer should have been: $x^2(3x+1)-3(3x+1)$.

3. $x^3+4x^2+5x+20 = (x^2+5)(x+4)$ The common factor in the first two terms is x^2 and the common factor in the last two terms is 5. Your interim answer should have been: $x^2(x+4)+5(x+4)$.

4. $12a^3+28a^2-15a-35 = (4a^2-5)(3a+7)$ The common factor in the first two terms is $4a^2$ and the common factor in the last two terms is –5. Your interim answer should have been: $4a^2(3a+7)-5(3a+7)$.

5. $6x^2-x-15$

Factors	Difference
90 and 1	89
45 and 2	43
30 and 3	27
18 and 5	13
15 and 6	9
10 and **9**	**1** ←

Develop your table of factors of 90 $(6 \bullet 15)$ and differences.

The correct factors are 10 and 9.
Split the middle term and rewrite as: $6x^2 \overset{-x}{-10x+9x} -15$
Factor by grouping: $2x(3x-5)+3(3x-5)$
Answer: $(2x+3)(3x-5)$

6. $12x^2-25x+12$

Factors	Sum
144 and 1	145
72 and 2	74
48 and 3	51
36 and 4	40
24 and 6	30
18 and 8	26
16 and **9**	**25** ←

Develop your table of factors of 144 $(12 \bullet 12)$ and sums.

The correct factors are 16 and 9.
Split the middle term and write as: $12x^2 \overset{-25x}{-16x-9x} +12$
Factor by grouping: $4x(3x-4)-3(3x-4)$
Answer: $(4x-3)(3x-4)$

7. $6x^2+11x-10$ Develop your table:

Factors	Difference
60 and 1	59
30 and 2	28
20 and 3	17
15 and **4**	**11** ←

The correct factors are 15 and 4. Note that there are other factors of 60, but you can stop writing factors once you have found the correct ones.
Split the middle term: $6x^2+15x-4x-10$
Factor by grouping: $3x(2x+5)-2(2x+5)$
Answer: $(3x-2)(2x+5)$

8. $10x^2-31x-14$ Develop your table:

Factors	Difference
140 and 1	139
70 and 2	68
35 and **4**	**31** ←

The correct factors are 35 and 4.
Split the middle term: $10x^2-35x+4x-14$
Factor by grouping: $5x(2x-7)+2(2x-7)$
Answer: $(5x+2)(2x-7)$

Lesson 9: Factoring Using Grouping

9. $6x^3 + 8x^2 + 2x$ This one has a common factor ($2x$), so we restate the problem as: $2x(3x^2 + 4x + 1)$

You can probably do this one without a factors table since the only factors are 3 and 1.

Answer: $2x(3x + 1)(x + 1)$

10. $8x^2 + 4x - 60$ This one also has a common factor (4), so we restate as: $4(2x^2 + x - 15)$

Can you also do this without a factor table? The product of 2 and 15 is 30 and the factors of 30 that have a difference of 1 are 6 and 5.

So, we split the middle term like this: $4(2x^2 + 6x - 5x - 15)$

And, we factor by grouping: $4[2x(x + 3) - 5(x + 3)]$

Answer: $4(2x - 5)(x + 3)$

Lesson 9: Factoring Using Grouping

Lesson 10: Solving Quadratic Equations by Factoring

In order to solve quadratic equations, we need to understand the **principle of zero products.** Earlier we learned that any number multiplied by zero results in an answer of zero: $a \bullet 0 = 0$. In other words, if the product of two numbers is zero, then one or both of the factors <u>must</u> be zero. Consider this example:

    Example 1.   Solve: $5x = 0$

The only solution to this problem is: $x = 0$

    Example 2.   Solve: $x \bullet y = 0$

In this case, we know that one of the variables, or both, have to be equal to zero. If $x = 0$, then y could be any value and the equation would still be true. Or, if $y = 0$, then x could be any value. Or, both x and y could be zero. This is the principle of zero products. Let's see how it works with some other equations.

    Example 3.   Solve: $x(x - 6) = 0$

The principle of zero products tells us that either factor could be zero, so we set each of the factors equal to zero and solve those equations. Like this:

$$x = 0 \qquad\qquad (x - 6) = 0$$

The first equation is already solved: $x = 0$. To solve the second equation, simply add 6 to each side and we find that $x = 6$.

So, our two possible solutions to this problem are $x = 0$ and $x = 6$. We can check the answers to see if we solved the problem correctly, by substituting these two values into the original equation.

$$x(x - 6) = 0 \qquad \text{First, substitute } x = 0.$$
$$0(0 - 6) = 0$$
$$0(-6) = 0$$
$$0 = 0 \qquad \text{Answer checks.} \quad$$

$$x(x - 6) = 0 \qquad \text{Second, substitute } x = 6.$$
$$6(6 - 6) = 0$$
$$6 \bullet 0 = 0$$
$$0 = 0 \qquad \text{Answer checks.} \quad$$

    Example 4.   Solve: $(x - 3)(x + 4) = 0$

$x - 3 = 0$	or	$x + 4 = 0$	Using the zero products principle, we set each factor equal to zero.
$x = 3$	or	$x = -4$	Then we solve each of these equations using the addition property learned earlier.

Now let's check these answers: Substitute $x = 3$ and $x = -4$ into $(x - 3)(x + 4) = 0$.

$$(3 - 3)(3 + 4) = 0 \qquad\qquad (-4 - 3)(-4 + 4) = 0$$
$$0 \bullet 7 = 0 \qquad\qquad\qquad -7 \bullet 0 = 0$$
$$0 = 0 \qquad\qquad\qquad\qquad 0 = 0 \qquad \text{Both values check.} \quad$$

Lesson 10: Solving Quadratic Equations by Factoring

Now that we have learned the principle of zero products, let's see how to take a quadratic equation and use factoring first and then the principle of zero products to solve the equation.

 Remember, "solving" means to find the x value or values that make the equation true.

Example 5. Solve: $x^2 + 5x + 6 = 0$

Our first step is to factor the quadratic expression using the knowledge gained in the last couple of lessons on factoring. We then rewrite the equation using the factors:

$$(x+2)(x+3) = 0$$

$$(x+2) = 0 \qquad\qquad (x+3) = 0 \qquad \text{Now set each factor equal to zero}$$
$$x = -2 \qquad\qquad\qquad x = -3 \qquad \text{and solve each equation.}$$

Now, let's try a few more examples, with each one having a different challenge.

Example 6. Solve: $9x^2 - 64 = 0$

You should recognize that this is the difference of squares and can be factored as:

$$(3x+8)(3x-8) = 0$$

$$3x + 8 = 0 \qquad \text{or} \qquad 3x - 8 = 0 \qquad \text{We then set each factor equal to zero.}$$

Solving these equations requires the use of both the addition and multiplication properties, and we get:

$$3x = -8 \quad \text{or} \quad 3x = 8$$
$$x = -\frac{8}{3} \quad \text{or} \quad x = \frac{8}{3}$$

Example 7. Solve: $4x^2 = 49$

Solving quadratic equations is different from solving linear equations. With linear equations, we try to isolate the variable on one side of the equation and put the constants on the other side. With quadratic equations, we want to get <u>all</u> terms on one side and have zero on the other side. Once all the terms are on one side, we write them in descending order of the exponents of the variable. This is the *standard form of a quadratic equation*: $ax^2 + bx + c = 0$. So, for **Example 7**, we use the addition property to move the constant term to the left and we get:

$$4x^2 - 49 = 0$$

Now we have the difference of squares on the left (like we had in the previous example), which is factorable as shown on the left.

$$(2x+7)(2x-7) = 0$$

$$2x + 7 = 0 \qquad \text{or} \qquad 2x - 7 = 0 \qquad\qquad \text{Set each factor equal to zero and solve.}$$

$$x = -\frac{7}{2} \qquad \text{or} \qquad x = \frac{7}{2}$$

Example 8. Solve: $2x^2 - 3x = 20$

Lesson 10: Solving Quadratic Equations by Factoring

As with the last example, we have to put this in standard format for a quadratic equation. We do this by moving the constant term to the left side of the equation, which gives us:

$$2x^2 - 3x - 20 = 0$$

$$2x^2 - 8x + 5x - 20 = 0$$
$$2x(x-4) + 5(x-4) = 0$$
$$(2x+5)(x-4) = 0$$

To factor this, we will use the grouping method. We multiply the coefficient of the first term and third term to get 40 and then look for factors of 40 such that the difference is 3 and those factors are 8 and 5. So we split the middle term.

$$2x + 5 = 0 \quad \text{or} \quad x - 4 = 0$$
$$x = -\frac{5}{2} \quad \text{or} \quad x = 4$$

Set each factor equal to zero and solve.

Example 9. Solve: $x^2 + x = 27 + 7x$

$$x^2 + x - 27 - 7x = 0$$
$$x^2 - 6x - 27 = 0$$

First step is to move all terms to the left side of the equation.

Then collect like terms.

$$(x-9)(x+3) = 0$$

Now, find factors of 27 such that their difference is 6. The factors are 9 and 3.

$$x = 9 \quad \text{or} \quad x = -3$$

Setting each factor to zero and solving gives us the solutions.

Now it's your turn.

Lesson 10: Solving Quadratic Equations by Factoring

Lesson 10: Solving Quadratic Equations by Factoring

Exercises

1. $7x(x-3) = 0$

2. $(y+4)(y+6) = 0$

3. $z^2 - 2z - 35 = 0$

4. $a^2 + 8a + 15 = 0$

5. $9x^2 - 100 = 0$

6. $4x^2 - 20x + 25 = 0$

7. $3x^2 - 5 = 2x$

8. $x^2 + 6x = 0$

9. $x^2 + 5x = -x - 5$

10. $0 = 36 + x^2 + 12x$

Lesson 10: Solving Quadratic Equations by Factoring

Solutions

1. $7x(x-3) = 0$ Set each factor equal to zero and solve.

         $7x = 0$ or $x - 3 = 0$

          $x = 0$ or $x = 3$

2. $(y+4)(y+6) = 0$ Set each factor equal to zero and solve.

         $y + 4 = 0$ or $y + 6 = 0$

          $y = -4$ or $y = -6$

3. $z^2 - 2z - 35 = 0$ Factor the quadratic expression first, then set the factors equal to zero and solve.

         $(z-7)(z+5) = 0$

         $z - 7 = 0$ or $z + 5 = 0$

          $z = 7$ or $z = -5$

4. $a^2 + 8a + 15 = 0$ Factor the quadratic expression first, then set the factors equal to zero and solve:

         $(a+5)(a+3) = 0$

         $a + 5 = 0$ or $a + 3 = 0$

          $a = -5$ or $a = -3$

5. $9x^2 - 100 = 0$ Did you recognize this expression as the difference of squares? Factor, then set

         $(3x-10)(3x+10) = 0$ the factors equal to zero and solve.

         $3x - 10 = 0$ or $3x + 10 = 0$

         $x = \pm\dfrac{10}{3}$ Notice that we have used a shorthand way ($\pm$) to write + and – the same quantity.

6. $4x^2 - 20x + 25 = 0$ Did you recognize this as a trinomial square?   We still proceed the same way:

         $(2x-5)^2 = 0$ factor, then set the factors equal to zero and solve.

         $2x - 5 = 0$ or $2x - 5 = 0$

             $x = \dfrac{5}{2}$ Both equations yield the same result, so there is only one answer.

7. $3x^2 - 5 = 2x$ First item of business is to put the quadratic equation in standard format, then

         $3x^2 - 2x - 5 = 0$ factor, and then set the factors equal to zero and solve.

         $(3x-5)(x+1) = 0$

         $3x - 5 = 0$ or $x + 1 = 0$

         $x = \dfrac{5}{3}$ or $x = -1$

8. $x^2 + 6x = 0$
    $x(x+6) = 0$
    $x = 0 \quad x + 6 = 0$
    $x = 0, -6$

    After putting the equation in the standard format, factor out the common factor of x. Set the factors equal to zero, and solve.

9. $x^2 + 5x = -x - 5$
    $x^2 + 6x + 5 = 0$
    $(x+5)(x+1) = 0$
    $x = -5, -1$

    Put in standard format by moving the terms on the right to the left using the addition property, then combine like terms, then factor, set the factors equal to zero, and solve:
    This is an acceptable way to write the answer.

10. $0 = 36 + x^2 + 12x$
    $0 = x^2 + 12x + 36$
    $0 = (x+6)^2$
    $x = -6$

    Even though the zero is on the left side of the equation, we don't have to move any terms from one side to the other. All the terms are already on one side of the equation – and it doesn't matter which side. We still have to put the expression into standard format. Notice that it is a trinomial square. Factor the trinomial square, set the factors equal to zero, and solve.

Lesson 10: Solving Quadratic Equations by Factoring

Lesson 11: Rational Expressions - Multiplication

Before we get started on operations with rational expressions, we need some more work on our vocabulary. You may remember from previous math experiences that *rational numbers* are quotients of integers, like:

Rational Numbers: $\quad\dfrac{5}{8}\qquad\qquad\dfrac{12}{17}\qquad\qquad\dfrac{-7}{15}\qquad\qquad\dfrac{22}{-9}$

Rational expressions are simply quotients of polynomials.

Rational Expressions: $\quad\dfrac{x+1}{x-1}\qquad\qquad\dfrac{x^2}{x+5}\qquad\qquad\dfrac{y^2-y-6}{y-3}$

Since polynomials also include constant terms, the rational numbers above are also rational expressions. We also refer to all the above examples as fractions since a fraction is also a quotient. Because of that, the rules for fractions also apply to rational expressions. As we discuss each of the operations and rational expressions, we will review the rules for fractions. This lesson will discuss multiplication.

Multiplication of Fractions

Multiplication of fractions is the simplest of operations involving fractions and that is why we deal with it first. When we have two fractions that are to be multiplied, all we do is multiply the numerator of the first fraction times the numerator of the second fraction, and the denominator of the first fraction times the denominator of the second. In general terms, it looks like this:

Example 1. Multiply $\quad\dfrac{a}{b}\bullet\dfrac{c}{d}=\dfrac{a\bullet c}{b\bullet d}$

With real numbers, it looks like this:

Example 2. Multiply: $\quad\dfrac{2}{5}\bullet\dfrac{3}{7}=\dfrac{2\bullet3}{5\bullet7}=\dfrac{6}{35}$

When we were working with fractions, you might remember we also looked for common factors. We called this process simplifying the fraction. It worked like this:

Example 3. Multiply and simplify: $\quad\dfrac{3}{5}\bullet\dfrac{15}{21}=\dfrac{3\bullet\cancel{3}\bullet\cancel{5}}{\cancel{5}\bullet\cancel{3}\bullet7}=\dfrac{3}{7}$

Multiplication of Rational Expressions

Multiplication of rational expressions and simplifying rational expressions works just like the above examples. **Example 4** shows the multiplication of rational expressions, while **Example 5** illustrates multiplication and simplification.

Example 4. Multiply: $\quad\dfrac{x}{y}\bullet\dfrac{2}{y}=\dfrac{2\bullet x}{y\bullet y}=\dfrac{2x}{y^2}$

Example 5. Multiply and simplify: $\quad\dfrac{8x}{3y}\bullet\dfrac{9y}{12x^2}=\dfrac{2\bullet\cancel{2}\bullet\cancel{2}\bullet\cancel{x}\bullet\cancel{3}\bullet3\bullet\cancel{y}}{\cancel{3}\bullet\cancel{y}\bullet\cancel{2}\bullet\cancel{2}\bullet\cancel{3}\bullet\cancel{x}\bullet x}=\dfrac{2}{x}$

Lesson 11: Rational Expressions - Multiplication

Here are a few more examples illustrating the multiplication and simplification process:

Example 6.   Multiply and simplify: $\dfrac{x^2-36}{6}\cdot\dfrac{10}{x-6}$

$\dfrac{(x-6)(x+6)}{6}\cdot\dfrac{10}{x-6}$

As we did in **Example 5** above, we factor all expressions that have factors and then look for common factors.

$=\dfrac{(x-6)(x+6)\cdot 5\cdot 2}{3\cdot 2(x-6)}$

Now we can "cancel" the common factors in the numerator and denominator.

$=\dfrac{5(x+6)}{3}$

Notice that there are two common factors, which results in our answer.

Example 7.   Multiply and simplify: $\dfrac{y^2-3y-10}{y-5}\cdot\dfrac{y-2}{y^2-4y+4}$

$\dfrac{(y-5)(y+2)}{y-5}\cdot\dfrac{y-2}{(y-2)(y-2)}$

The numerator of the first rational expression and the denominator of the second can be factored so the problem can be restated.

$=\dfrac{(y-5)(y+2)(y-2)}{(y-5)(y-2)(y-2)}$

$=\dfrac{y+2}{y-2}$

There are two common factors so the answer is simplified.

Example 8.   Multiply and simplify: $\dfrac{8t^2}{3t^2-12t+12}\cdot\dfrac{6t-12}{2t}$

$\dfrac{8t^2}{3(t-2)(t-2)}\cdot\dfrac{6(t-2)}{2t}$

Restate the problem after factoring all expressions that can be factored, then multiply and simplify.

$=\dfrac{2\cdot 2\cdot 2\cdot 2\cdot 3\cdot t\cdot t(t-2)}{3\cdot 2\cdot t(t-2)(t-2)}$

$=\dfrac{8t}{t-2}$

The simplified answer.

Example 9.   Multiply and simplify: $\dfrac{a}{a^2-4} \bullet \dfrac{a^2-5a+6}{a^2-3a}$

$$\frac{a}{(a-2)(a+2)} \bullet \frac{(a-2)(a-3)}{a(a-3)} = \frac{\cancel{a}\cancel{(a-2)}\cancel{(a-3)}}{\cancel{a}\cancel{(a-2)}(a+2)\cancel{(a-3)}}$$

Again, factor all expressions that are factorable and then restate the problem, multiply, then simplify.

Since all three terms in the numerator have been "cancelled", what does that leave in the numerator? Remember when we cancel, we are actually dividing a factor by itself, leaving one.

So, our answer is: $\dfrac{1}{a+2}$

Now you give it a try.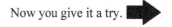

Lesson 11: Rational Expressions - Multiplication

Lesson 11: Rational Expressions - Multiplication

Exercises: Multiply and simplify.

1. $\dfrac{3}{7} \bullet \dfrac{x}{y}$

2. $\dfrac{3x}{4y} \bullet \dfrac{x+1}{y}$

3. $\dfrac{2x^2}{5} \bullet \dfrac{10}{2x^4}$

4. $\dfrac{2a^2}{3a+6} \bullet \dfrac{a+2}{a}$

5. $\dfrac{a^2-25}{4a} \bullet \dfrac{8a^2}{a+5}$

6. $\dfrac{x^2-8x+15}{x^2-16} \bullet \dfrac{x+4}{x-5}$

7. $\dfrac{x^2+6x-7}{x^2-1} \bullet \dfrac{x+1}{x+7}$

8. $\dfrac{x^2-7x+10}{x^2-25} \bullet \dfrac{x+2}{x^2-4}$

9. $\dfrac{2y^2-72}{6y^2-24} \bullet \dfrac{8y+8}{24y-144}$

10. $\dfrac{3x-6}{x^2-x-6} \bullet \dfrac{x^2+5x+6}{2x+6}$

Lesson 11: Rational Expressions - Multiplication

Solutions:

1. $\dfrac{3}{7} \cdot \dfrac{x}{y} = \dfrac{3x}{7y}$ Straight forward multiplication, with no simplification.

2. $\dfrac{3x}{4y} \cdot \dfrac{x+1}{y} = \dfrac{3x(x+1)}{4y^2}$ Straight forward multiplication, with no simplification.

3. $\dfrac{2x^2}{5} \cdot \dfrac{10}{2x^4} = \dfrac{2 \bullet x \bullet x \bullet 2 \bullet 5}{5 \bullet 2 \bullet x \bullet x \bullet x \bullet x} = \dfrac{2}{x^2}$ Rewrite showing all factors, then cancel common factors.

4. $\dfrac{2a^2}{3a+6} \cdot \dfrac{a+2}{a} = \dfrac{2 \bullet a \bullet a(a+2)}{3(a+2) \bullet a} = \dfrac{2a}{3}$ Rewrite showing all factors, then cancel common factors.

5. $\dfrac{a^2-25}{4a} \cdot \dfrac{8a^2}{a+5} = \dfrac{(a-5)(a+5)2 \bullet 2 \bullet 2 \bullet a \bullet a}{2 \bullet 2 \bullet a(a+5)}$ Rewrite showing all factors, then cancel common factors.

   $\dfrac{2a(a-5)}{1} = 2a(a-5)$ All the factors in the denominator have been cancelled, but remember that when we cancel, we are actually dividing a term by itself, leaving a value of one.

6. $\dfrac{x^2-8x+15}{x^2-16} \cdot \dfrac{x+4}{x-5} = \dfrac{(x-5)(x-3)(x+4)}{(x-4)(x+4)(x-5)} = \dfrac{x-3}{x-4}$ Rewrite showing all factors, then cancel common factors.

7. $\dfrac{x^2+6x-7}{x^2-1} \cdot \dfrac{x+1}{x+7} = \dfrac{(x+7)(x-1)(x+1)}{(x-1)(x+1)(x+7)} = \dfrac{1}{1} = 1$ Rewrite showing all factors, then cancel common factors. Here all factors cancel leaving one in the numerator and denominator, so the answer is one.

8. $\dfrac{x^2-7x+10}{x^2-25} \cdot \dfrac{x+2}{x^2-4} = \dfrac{(x-5)(x-2)(x+2)}{(x-5)(x+5)(x-2)(x+2)} = \dfrac{1}{x+5}$ Rewrite showing all factors, then cancel common factors. This time all factors in the numerator have been cancelled, which leaves one in the numerator.

9. $\dfrac{2y^2-72}{6y^2-24} \cdot \dfrac{8y+8}{24y-144} = \dfrac{2(y+6)(y-6) \bullet 2 \bullet 2 \bullet 2 \bullet (y+1)}{3 \bullet 2(y-2)(y+2) \bullet 2 \bullet 2 \bullet 2 \bullet 3 \bullet (y-6)}$ This one requires a lot of factoring

   After canceling, we have: $\dfrac{(y+6)(y+1)}{9(y+2)(y-2)}$

10. $\dfrac{3x-6}{x^2-x-6} \cdot \dfrac{x^2+5x+6}{2x+6} = \dfrac{3(x-2)(x+2)(x+3)}{(x-3)(x+2)(x+3)2} = \dfrac{3(x-2)}{2(x-3)}$ Rewrite showing all factors, then cancel common factors.

Lesson 12: Rational Expressions - Division

As with multiplication of rational expressions, we begin our discussion of division of rational expression with a review of how we divide fractions. In dividing fractions, multiply the first fraction by the reciprocal of the second fraction. Remember what a reciprocal is? It means we "flip" the fraction. Let's do a few reciprocal examples first:

Example 1. The reciprocal of $\dfrac{2}{5}$ is $\dfrac{5}{2}$

Example 2. The reciprocal of $\dfrac{x}{x+1}$ is $\dfrac{x+1}{x}$

Now let's try some try some examples of division of fractions before we tackle division of rational expressions. In general, it looks like this:

Example 3. Divide: $\dfrac{a}{b} \div \dfrac{c}{d} = \dfrac{a}{b} \bullet \dfrac{d}{c} = \dfrac{a \bullet d}{b \bullet c}$

With numbers, it looks like this:

Example 4. Divide: $\dfrac{3}{4} \div \dfrac{2}{5} = \dfrac{3}{4} \bullet \dfrac{5}{2} = \dfrac{3 \bullet 5}{4 \bullet 2} = \dfrac{15}{8}$

Once we have changed the problem from a division problem to a multiplication problem by taking the reciprocal of the second term, we can look for common factors to cancel as in the following example.

Example 5. Divide and simplify: $\dfrac{4}{5} \div \dfrac{12}{25} = \dfrac{4}{5} \bullet \dfrac{25}{12} = \dfrac{\cancel{2} \bullet \cancel{2} \bullet \cancel{5} \bullet 5}{\cancel{5} \bullet \cancel{2} \bullet \cancel{2} \bullet 3} = \dfrac{5}{3}$

Now let's do some division with rational expressions:

Example 6. Divide and simplify: $\dfrac{3x}{4} \div \dfrac{x^2}{8}$

$\dfrac{3x}{4} \bullet \dfrac{8}{x^2} = \dfrac{3 \bullet \cancel{x} \bullet \cancel{2} \bullet \cancel{2} \bullet 2}{\cancel{2} \bullet \cancel{2} \bullet \cancel{x} \bullet x} = \dfrac{6}{x}$

Rewrite as a multiplication problem by taking the reciprocal of the second term, then look to simplify.

Now we'll try one with a little factoring involved:

Example 7. Divide and simplify: $\dfrac{a^2-1}{a^2} \div \dfrac{a-1}{a+1}$

$\dfrac{(a+1)(a-1)}{a \bullet a} \bullet \dfrac{a+1}{a-1} = \dfrac{(a+1)\cancel{(a-1)}(a+1)}{a \bullet a\cancel{(a-1)}} = \dfrac{(a+1)^2}{a^2}$

Example 8. Divide and simplify: $\dfrac{x^2+4x}{x^2+3x-4} \div \dfrac{x}{x+1}$

In one step, we will factor the numerator and denominator of the first rational expression and take the reciprocal of the second term turning the problem into a multiplication problem.

$$\frac{x(x+4)}{(x+4)(x-1)} \bullet \frac{x+1}{x} = \frac{\cancel{x}\cancel{(x+4)}(x+1)}{\cancel{x}\cancel{(x+4)}(x-1)} = \frac{x+1}{x-1}$$

Now cancel out the common factors.

Sometimes all terms require factoring, like this next example:

Example 9. Divide and simplify: $\dfrac{x^2-7x+12}{x^2+x-20} \div \dfrac{x^2-6x+9}{x^2+10x+25}$

Since there are many factors involved, we will do this one in two steps. We will first rewrite the problem as a multiplication problem taking the reciprocal of the second term:

$$\frac{x^2-7x+12}{x^2+x-20} \bullet \frac{x^2+10x+25}{x^2-6x+9}$$

Now we will factor all the expressions, and simplify:

$$\frac{\cancel{(x-3)}\cancel{(x-4)}}{\cancel{(x+5)}\cancel{(x-4)}} \bullet \frac{\cancel{(x+5)}(x+5)}{\cancel{(x-3)}(x-3)} = \frac{x+5}{x-3}$$

Now it's your turn. ➡

Lesson 12: Rational Expressions - Division

Exercises

1. Find the reciprocal of: $\dfrac{3x-5}{x+2}$

2. Divide: $\dfrac{4x}{y} \div \dfrac{15y}{2}$

3. Divide and simplify: $\dfrac{3y}{4x} \div \dfrac{9y^2}{8}$

4. Divide and simplify: $\dfrac{6a^2}{5b} \div \dfrac{18a}{5b^2}$

5. Divide and simplify: $\dfrac{a^2-25}{a^2} \div \dfrac{a+5}{a}$

6. Divide and simplify: $\dfrac{x^2-x-6}{15} \div \dfrac{x-3}{5x-10}$

7. Divide and simplify: $\dfrac{y-4}{y^2-3y-4} \div \dfrac{2}{y+1}$

8. Divide and simplify: $\dfrac{x^2+8x+15}{x^2+6x+9} \div \dfrac{x+5}{x+3}$

9. Divide and simplify: $\dfrac{x^2-49}{x^2-3x-28} \div \dfrac{x}{x^2+6x+8}$

10. Divide and simplify: $\dfrac{x^4-1}{4x+4} \div \dfrac{x^2+1}{2}$

Lesson 12: Rational Expressions - Division

Solutions

1.　Find the reciprocal of:　　$\dfrac{3x-5}{x+2}$　　Answer: $\dfrac{x+2}{3x-5}$

Reciprocal means to "flip" the fraction, making the numerator move to the denominator and the denominator to the numerator.

2.　Divide:　　$\dfrac{4x}{y} \div \dfrac{15y}{2} = \dfrac{4x}{y} \cdot \dfrac{2}{15y} = \dfrac{8x}{15y^2}$

Take the reciprocal and multiply.

3.　Divide and simplify:　　$\dfrac{3y}{4x} \div \dfrac{9y^2}{8} = \dfrac{3y}{4x} \cdot \dfrac{8}{9y^2} = \dfrac{\cancel{3} \cdot \cancel{y} \cdot \cancel{2} \cdot \cancel{2} \cdot 2}{\cancel{2} \cdot \cancel{2} \cdot x \cdot \cancel{3} \cdot 3 \cdot \cancel{y} \cdot y} = \dfrac{2}{3xy}$

Take the reciprocal and multiply, then cancel common factors.

4.　Divide and simplify:　　$\dfrac{6a^2}{5b} \div \dfrac{18a}{5b^2} = \dfrac{6a^2}{5b} \cdot \dfrac{5b^2}{18a} = \dfrac{\cancel{2} \cdot \cancel{3} \cdot \cancel{a} \cdot a \cdot \cancel{5} \cdot \cancel{b} \cdot b}{\cancel{5} \cdot \cancel{b} \cdot \cancel{2} \cdot \cancel{3} \cdot 3 \cdot \cancel{a}} = \dfrac{ab}{3}$

Take the reciprocal and multiply, then cancel common factors.

5.　Divide and simplify:　　$\dfrac{a^2-25}{a^2} \div \dfrac{a+5}{a} = \dfrac{a^2-25}{a^2} \cdot \dfrac{a}{a+5} = \dfrac{(a+5)(a-5)\cancel{a}}{\cancel{a} \cdot a(a+5)}$

Take the reciprocal and multiply, then cancel common factors and the answer is:

$$= \dfrac{a-5}{a}$$

Note that the a's do not cancel out. The variable a is not a factor in the numerator.

6.   Divide and simplify:
$$\frac{x^2-x-6}{15}\div\frac{x-3}{5x-10}=\frac{x^2-x-6}{15}\bullet\frac{5x-10}{x-3}$$
$$=\frac{(x-3)(x+2)}{15}\bullet\frac{5(x-2)}{x-3}=\frac{\cancel{5}\cancel{(x-3)}(x+2)(x-2)}{3\bullet\cancel{5}\cancel{(x-3)}}$$

Answer:
$$=\frac{(x+2)(x-2)}{3}$$

The answer may be left in the factored form.

7.   Divide and simplify:
$$\frac{y-4}{y^2-3y-4}\div\frac{2}{y+1}=\frac{y-4}{y^2-3y-4}\bullet\frac{y+1}{2}$$
$$=\frac{\cancel{(y-4)}\cancel{(y+1)}}{\cancel{(y-4)}\cancel{(y+1)}2}=\frac{1}{2}$$

Remember that even though all the terms in the numerator have been cancelled, the numerator is one.

8.   Divide and simplify:
$$\frac{x^2+8x+15}{x^2+6x+9}\div\frac{x+5}{x+3}=\frac{\cancel{(x+3)}\cancel{(x+5)}}{\cancel{(x+3)}\cancel{(x+3)}}\bullet\frac{\cancel{x+3}}{\cancel{x+5}}=\frac{1}{1}=1$$

When we finish canceling out common terms, we are left with a one in the numerator and one in the denominator, so the answer is one.

9.   Divide and simplify:
$$\frac{x^2-49}{x^2-3x-28}\div\frac{x}{x^2+6x+8}=\frac{\cancel{(x-7)}(x+7)}{\cancel{(x-7)}\cancel{(x+4)}}\bullet\frac{(x+2)\cancel{(x+4)}}{x}$$
$$=\frac{(x+7)(x+2)}{x}$$

10.   Divide and simplify:
$$\frac{x^4-1}{4x+4}\div\frac{x^2+1}{2}=\frac{x^4-1}{4x+4}\bullet\frac{2}{x^2+1}$$

Factor completely!
$$=\frac{\cancel{(x^2+1)}\cancel{(x+1)}(x-1)\cancel{2}}{\cancel{2}\bullet2\cancel{(x+1)}\cancel{(x^2+1)}}=\frac{x-1}{2}$$

Let's review how we add and subtract fractions before we dive into how it's done for rational expressions. Remember we can't add or subtract fractions unless they are like fractions – meaning they have to have the same denominator. If they don't have the same denominator, we have to convert them to like fractions. Here is the general rule for adding or subtracting fractions:

Example 1. $\dfrac{a}{b}+\dfrac{c}{b}=\dfrac{a+c}{b}$ and $\dfrac{a}{b}-\dfrac{c}{b}=\dfrac{a-c}{b}$

With integers, it looks like this:

Example 2. Add: $\dfrac{1}{5}+\dfrac{2}{5}=\dfrac{3}{5}$ Since these are "like fractions" they can be added and when we add fractions, we add the numerators and put the result over the common denominator.

If the denominators are not alike, we rewrite the fractions as like fractions.
Here is an example of adding unlike fractions:

Example 3. Add: $\dfrac{1}{6}+\dfrac{3}{8}$

Factorization of 6: $2\bullet 3$
Factorization of 8: $2\bullet 2\bullet 2$
LCD: $2\bullet 2\bullet 2\bullet 3 = 24$

To write equivalent fractions we have to find the least common denominator, and the method recommended in an earlier section was the prime factorization method. Using that method we find the prime factorization of each denominator and the LCD is then found by taking each factor the greatest number of times it appears in any factorization.

$\dfrac{1}{6}\bullet\dfrac{4}{4}=\dfrac{4}{24}$ $\dfrac{3}{8}\bullet\dfrac{3}{3}=\dfrac{9}{24}$

Now, we rewrite each fraction as an equivalent fraction with a denominator of 24.

$\dfrac{4}{24}+\dfrac{9}{24}=\dfrac{13}{24}$ Next, we add the equivalent fractions.

Now that we have reviewed addition of fractions (subtraction is done the same way), we will proceed with the addition and subtraction of rational expressions.

Example 4. Add: $\dfrac{x}{y}+\dfrac{3}{y}=\dfrac{x+3}{y}$

Since these rational expressions (fractions) have the same denominator, they are "like fractions" and we do not need to write equivalent fractions or expressions. We simply add their numerators and write the result over the denominator.

Example 5. Subtract: $\dfrac{x}{z}-\dfrac{3}{z}=\dfrac{x-3}{z}$

Subtraction is done the same way. These are like fractions and the numerators can be subtracted with the result written over the denominator.

Example 6.   Add: $\dfrac{5}{6x^2} + \dfrac{4}{9x^3}$

These rational expressions don't have a common denominator so we have to find it and write equivalent fractions:

$$\text{Factorization of } 6x^2 = 2 \bullet 3 \bullet x \bullet x$$
$$\text{Factorization of } 9x^3 = 3 \bullet 3 \bullet x \bullet x \bullet x$$
$$\text{LCD:} \quad 2 \bullet 3 \bullet 3 \bullet x \bullet x \bullet x = 18x^3$$

$$\dfrac{5}{6x^2} \bullet \dfrac{3x}{3x} = \dfrac{15x}{18x^3} \qquad\qquad \dfrac{4}{9x^3} \bullet \dfrac{2}{2} = \dfrac{8}{18x^3} \qquad \text{Now, we write equivalent fractions.}$$

$$\dfrac{15x}{18x^3} + \dfrac{8}{18x^3} = \dfrac{15x+8}{18x^3} \qquad \text{Then, add.}$$

Sometimes after adding or subtracting, we will have common factors in the numerator and denominator and we will have to simplify the expression, just like we always had to reduce fractions to their lowest terms. Let's try an example that illustrates this:

Example 7.   Add: $\dfrac{2x}{x^2-1} + \dfrac{1}{x^2+x}$

Factorization of $x^2 - 1: (x+1)(x-1)$ Since the expressions do not have the same

Factorization of $x^2 + x: x(x+1)$ denominator, we have to find a LCD and write

LCD: $x(x+1)(x-1)$ equivalent fractions.

Equivalent expressions: $\dfrac{2x}{(x+1)(x-1)} \bullet \dfrac{x}{x} = \dfrac{2x^2}{x(x+1)(x-1)}$

$$\dfrac{1}{x(x+1)} \bullet \dfrac{x-1}{x-1} = \dfrac{x-1}{x(x+1)(x-1)}$$

The sum of these two expressions is: $\dfrac{2x^2+x-1}{x(x+1)(x-1)} = \dfrac{(2x-1)(x+1)}{x(x+1)(x-1)} = \dfrac{2x-1}{x(x-1)}$

We simplify by factoring the numerator and dividing common factors.

As mentioned earlier, subtraction follows the same process: If the denominators are different, then find a LCD, write equivalent fractions, and then subtract the numerators. Look for common factors so the expression is written in its simplest form. The only difficulty is in subtracting numerators that may contain several terms. Remember when we subtracted polynomials? Here is a quick refresher:

Example 8. Subtract: $(x^2 - 4x + 6) - (3x^2 - 5x + 2)$

When subtracting polynomials, we have to change the sign of each term you are subtracting, so the problem becomes:

$$x^2 - 4x + 6 - 3x^2 + 5x - 2 = -2x^2 + x + 4$$

Now, let's try a subtraction problem with rational expressions:

Example 9. Subtract: $\dfrac{4x}{y} - \dfrac{3x-2}{y} = \dfrac{4x-(3x-2)}{y} = \dfrac{4x-3x+2}{y} = \dfrac{x+2}{y}$

If the denominators are different, we have to find the LCD, then write equivalent fractions and then subtract. Let's try one like that.

Example 10. Subtract: $\dfrac{3x}{4x^2} - \dfrac{6+x}{6x^3}$

Factorization of $4x^2 : 2 \bullet 2 \bullet x \bullet x$
Factorization of $6x^3 : 2 \bullet 3 \bullet x \bullet x \bullet x$
LCD: $2 \bullet 2 \bullet 3 \bullet x \bullet x \bullet x = 12x^3$

Equivalent expressions: $\dfrac{3x}{4x^2} \bullet \dfrac{3x}{3x} = \dfrac{9x^2}{12x^3}$ $\qquad \dfrac{6+x}{6x^3} \bullet \dfrac{2}{2} = \dfrac{12+2x}{12x^3}$

Subtract the expressions: $\dfrac{9x^2}{12x^3} - \dfrac{12+2x}{12x^3} = \dfrac{9x^2-(12+2x)}{12x^3} = \dfrac{9x^2-2x-12}{12x^3}$

Example 11. Subtract: $\dfrac{y}{y^2+5y+6} - \dfrac{2}{y^2+3y+2}$

Factorization of $y^2 + 5y + 6 : (y+2)(y+3)$
Factorization of $y^2 + 3y + 2 : (y+1)(y+2)$
LCD: $(y+1)(y+2)(y+3)$

Equivalent expressions: $\dfrac{y}{(y+2)(y+3)} \bullet \dfrac{(y+1)}{(y+1)} = \dfrac{y(y+1)}{(y+1)(y+2)(y+3)}$

$$\dfrac{2}{(y+1)(y+2)} \bullet \dfrac{(y+3)}{(y+3)} = \dfrac{2(y+3)}{(y+1)(y+2)(y+3)}$$

Subtract the expressions: $\dfrac{y(y+1)-2(y+3)}{(y+1)(y+2)(y+3)} = \dfrac{y^2+y-2y-6}{(y+1)(y+2)(y+3)}$

Collect like terms in the numerator, then factor, and cancel any common factors:

$$= \frac{y^2 - y - 6}{(y+1)(y+2)(y+3)} = \frac{(y-3)(y+2)}{(y+1)(y+2)(y+3)}$$

This results in the answer of:

$$= \frac{(y-3)}{(y+1)(y+3)}$$

Now you try some. ➡

76

Exercises: Simplify.

1. $\dfrac{3x}{x+2}+\dfrac{2x}{x+2}$

2. $\dfrac{4y}{y-3}-\dfrac{2y}{y-3}$

3. $\dfrac{6}{5x}+\dfrac{3x}{4x^2}$

4. $\dfrac{7}{3x^2}-\dfrac{2x}{5x}$

5. $\dfrac{3y^2}{4}+\dfrac{4}{y}$

6. $\dfrac{5}{6y}-\dfrac{2}{5y^2}$

7. $\dfrac{4}{7x}-\dfrac{3x-1}{3x^2}$

8. $\dfrac{5}{3x^2}-\dfrac{2x+1}{4x^3}$

9. $\dfrac{x}{x^2+5x+6}+\dfrac{3}{x^2-2x-8}$

10. $\dfrac{2x}{x^2-25}-\dfrac{(x+1)}{x^2+6x+5}$

Solutions

1. $\dfrac{3x}{x+2} + \dfrac{2x}{x+2} = \dfrac{3x+2x}{x+2} = \dfrac{5x}{x+2}$ These are like fractions so add the numerators.

2. $\dfrac{4y}{y-3} - \dfrac{2y}{y-3} = \dfrac{4y-2y}{y-3} = \dfrac{2y}{y-3}$ These are like fractions so subtract the numerators.

3. $\dfrac{6}{5x} + \dfrac{3x}{4x^2}$

    Factorization of $5x$: $5 \bullet x$

    Factorization of $4x^2$: $2 \bullet 2 \bullet x \bullet x$

    LCD: $5 \bullet 2 \bullet 2 \bullet x \bullet x = 20x^2$

    Equivalent fractions: $\dfrac{6}{5x} \bullet \dfrac{4x}{4x} = \dfrac{24x}{20x^2}$ $\dfrac{3x}{4x^2} \bullet \dfrac{5}{5} = \dfrac{15x}{20x^2}$

    Add the expressions and cancel like terms $\dfrac{24x}{20x^2} + \dfrac{15x}{20x^2} = \dfrac{39x}{20x^2} = \dfrac{39\cancel{x}}{20x \bullet \cancel{x}} = \dfrac{39}{20x}$

4. $\dfrac{7}{3x^2} - \dfrac{2x}{5x}$

    Factorization of $3x^2$: $3 \bullet x \bullet x$

    Factorization of $5x$: $5 \bullet x$

    LCD: $3 \bullet 5 \bullet x \bullet x = 15x^2$

    Equivalent fractions: $\dfrac{7}{3x^2} \bullet \dfrac{5}{5} = \dfrac{35}{15x^2}$ $\dfrac{2x}{5x} \bullet \dfrac{3x}{3x} = \dfrac{6x^2}{15x^2}$

    Subtract the expressions: $\dfrac{35}{15x^2} - \dfrac{6x^2}{15x^2} = \dfrac{35-6x^2}{15x^2}$

5. $\dfrac{3y^2}{4} + \dfrac{4}{y}$

    LCD: $2 \bullet 2 \bullet y = 4y$

    Equivalent fractions: $\dfrac{3y^2}{4} \bullet \dfrac{y}{y} = \dfrac{3y^3}{4y}$ $\dfrac{4}{y} \bullet \dfrac{4}{4} = \dfrac{16}{4y}$

    Add the expressions: $\dfrac{3y^3}{4y} + \dfrac{16}{4y} = \dfrac{3y^3+16}{4y}$

6. $\dfrac{5}{6y} - \dfrac{2}{5y^2}$

    Factorization of $6y$: $2 \bullet 3 \bullet y$

    Factorization of $5y^2$: $5 \bullet y \bullet y$

    LCD: $2 \bullet 3 \bullet 5 \bullet y \bullet y = 30y^2$

    Equivalent fractions: $\dfrac{5}{6y} \bullet \dfrac{5y}{5y} = \dfrac{25y}{30y^2}$ $\dfrac{2}{5y^2} \bullet \dfrac{6}{6} = \dfrac{12}{30y^2}$

    Subtract the expressions: $\dfrac{25y}{30y^2} - \dfrac{12}{30y^2} = \dfrac{25y-12}{30y^2}$

7. $\dfrac{4}{7x} - \dfrac{3x-1}{3x^2}$

Equivalent fractions: $\dfrac{4}{7x} \bullet \dfrac{3x}{3x} = \dfrac{12x}{21x^2}$

Factorization of $7x : 7 \bullet x$

Factorization of $3x^2 : 3 \bullet x \bullet x$

LCD: $7 \bullet 3 \bullet x \bullet x = 21x^2$

$\dfrac{3x-1}{3x^2} \bullet \dfrac{7}{7} = \dfrac{7(3x-1)}{21x^2}$

Subtract the expressions: $\dfrac{12x}{21x^2} - \dfrac{7(3x-1)}{21x^2} = \dfrac{12x - 7(3x-1)}{21x^2} = \dfrac{12x - 21x + 7}{21x^2} = \dfrac{-9x+7}{21x^2}$

8. $\dfrac{5}{3x^2} - \dfrac{2x+1}{4x^3}$

Factorization of $3x^2 : 3 \bullet x \bullet x$

Factorization of $4x^3 : 2 \bullet 2 \bullet x \bullet x \bullet x$

LCD: $2 \bullet 2 \bullet 3 \bullet x \bullet x \bullet x = 12x^3$

Equivalent expressions: $\dfrac{5}{3x^2} \bullet \dfrac{4x}{4x} = \dfrac{20x}{12x^3}$

$\dfrac{2x+1}{4x^3} \bullet \dfrac{3}{3} = \dfrac{3(2x+1)}{12x^3}$

Subtract the expressions: $\dfrac{20x}{12x^3} - \dfrac{3(2x+1)}{12x^3} = \dfrac{20x - 6x - 3}{12x^3} = \dfrac{14x-3}{12x^3}$

9. $\dfrac{x}{x^2+5x+6} + \dfrac{3}{x^2-2x-8}$

Factorization of $x^2+5x+6 : (x+2)(x+3)$

Factorization of $x^2-2x-8 : (x-4)(x+2)$

LCD: $(x+2)(x+3)(x-4)$

Equivalent expressions: $\dfrac{x}{(x+2)(x+3)} \bullet \dfrac{(x-4)}{(x-4)} = \dfrac{x(x-4)}{(x+2)(x+3)(x-4)}$

$\dfrac{3}{(x-4)(x+2)} \bullet \dfrac{(x+3)}{(x+3)} = \dfrac{3(x+3)}{(x+2)(x+3)(x-4)}$

Add the expressions: $\dfrac{x^2-4x}{LCD} + \dfrac{3x+9}{LCD} = \dfrac{x^2-x+9}{(x+2)(x+3)(x-4)}$

10. $\dfrac{2x}{x^2-25}-\dfrac{(x+1)}{x^2+6x+5}$

Factorization of $x^2-25:(x-5)(x+5)$

Factorization of $x^2+6x+5:(x+5)(x+1)$

LCD: $\quad(x-5)(x+5)(x+1)$

Equivalent expressions: $\quad\dfrac{2x}{(x-5)(x+5)}\bullet\dfrac{(x+1)}{(x+1)}=\dfrac{2x(x+1)}{(x-5)(x+5)(x+1)}$

$$\dfrac{(x+1)}{(x+5)(x+1)}\bullet\dfrac{(x-5)}{(x-5)}=\dfrac{(x+1)(x-5)}{(x-5)(x+5)(x+1)}$$

Subtract the expressions: $\quad\dfrac{2x^2+2x}{LCD}-\dfrac{(x^2-4x-5)}{LCD}=\dfrac{x^2+6x+5}{LCD}$

This can be further simplified: $\quad=\dfrac{(x\!\!\!\diagup+1)(x\!\!\!\diagup+5)}{(x-5)(x\!\!\!\diagup+5)(x\!\!\!\diagup+1)}=\dfrac{1}{(x-5)}$

Lesson 14: Systems of Equations - Graphing

In the next three lessons, we will talk about three ways to solve a system of two linear equations in two unknowns. The first way is by graphing. Since a linear equation in two unknowns indicates a line, a system of two linear equations indicates two lines. The solution of the system is the point of intersection for those lines. The ordered pair that represents that point of intersection solves both equations. That means if you substituted the x and y values from the ordered pair into each of the two equations, you would find that it is a valid solution for both equations. Let's see how it works.

Example 1. Solve this system of equations by graphing: (1) $x + y = 5$

(2) $y = x + 3$

Remember how to graph lines? Develop a list of three points for each line by selecting a value for one of the variables and solving for the other.

(1) $x + y = 5$ (2) $y = x + 3$

x	y
0	5
2	3
4	1

x	y
0	3
-3	0
2	5

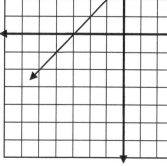

Notice that the point of intersection is (1,4). If we substitute this point into the above equations, we find that it is a solution of both equations. In fact, it is the <u>only</u> solution because the lines intersect in only one point.

(1)	$x + y = 5$	(2)	$y = x + 3$
	$1 + 4 = 5$		$4 = 1 + 3$
	$5 = 5$		$4 = 4$ ✓

Let's try another example:

Example 2. Solve this system of equations by graphing: (1) $2y = x + 8$

(2) $y = -2x - 6$

We begin by setting up our table of points for each equation and then graphing the lines.

(1) $2y = x + 8$ (2) $y = -2x - 6$

x	y
0	4
-2	3
-6	1

x	y
0	-6
-1	-4
-2	-2

Plot the points to get the graphs of both lines.

81

Lesson 14: Systems of Equations - Graphing

The point of intersection this time is (-4,2). Let's verify that this is the correct solution by substituting these values into the original equations.

(1) $2y = x + 8$
     $2 \bullet 2 = -4 + 8$
     $4 = 4$

(2) $y = -2x - 6$
     $2 = -2(-4) - 6$
     $2 = 2$

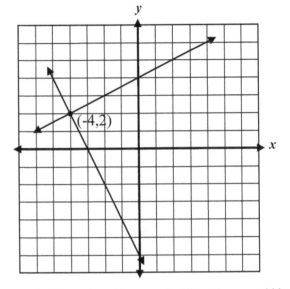

Not all systems of equations work out this nicely. For example, if we plotted two parallel lines there would be no point of intersection. Or, if we plotted the same line twice it would have an infinite number of points of intersection.

The problem with solving systems of equations by graphing is that the accuracy of the graph is difficult, particularly if the point of intersection involves fractions. So, graphing is the least preferred method of solving a system of equations. After graphing a few systems yourself you will see the difficulty in this method.

Now you practice your new graphing skills.

82

Lesson 14: Systems of Equations - Graphing

Exercises

1.   Solve this system of equations by graphing: (1) $y = 3x - 5$

(2) $y = -x + 3$

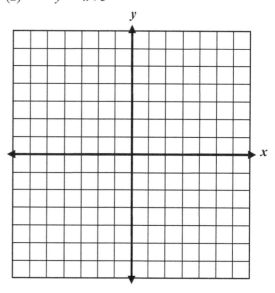

2.   Solve this system of equations by graphing: (1) $y = 2x + 1$

(2) $3x + y = -9$

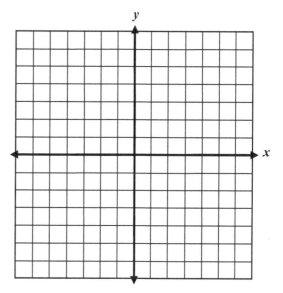

Lesson 14: Systems of Equations - Graphing

Solutions

1. Solve this system of equations by graphing:

    (1) $y = 3x - 5$

    (2) $y = -x + 3$

(1) $y = 3x - 5$ (2) $y = -x + 3$

x	y
0	-5
1	-2
3	4

x	y
0	3
1	2
4	-1

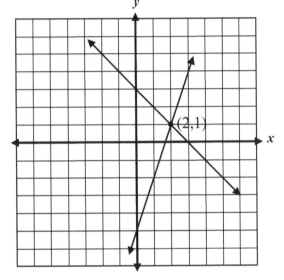

Point of intersection for the system of equations in problem 1 is **(2,1)**.

2. Solve this system of equations by graphing:

    (1) $y = 2x + 1$

    (2) $3x + y = -9$

(1) $y = 2x + 1$ (2) $3x + y = -9$

x	y
0	1
1	3
2	5

x	y
-3	0
-4	3
-5	6

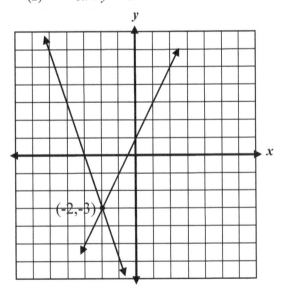

Point of intersection for the system of equations in problem 2 is **(-2,-3)**.

Lesson 15: Systems of Equations - The Substitution Method

In the previous lesson, we mentioned that there were three methods of solving systems of equations that we were going to discuss. We discussed the graphing method in the last lesson and you saw that this method had its limitations in accuracy. So, we need other methods to find the solution to systems of equations. The method to be discussed in this section is the **substitution method**. Here's an example of how it works:

Example 1.   Solve by substitution: (1) $y - 2x = -1$

(2) $x = y + 2$

The substitution method says that we express one of the variables in terms of the other and substitute that expression in the other equation. Sounds confusing, so let's see how it works with this example. In equation (2), we have x in terms of y ($x = y + 2$). The value of x is $y + 2$. So, we substitute $y + 2$ for x in equation (1). This gives us:

$$(1) \qquad y - 2x = -1$$
$$y - 2(y + 2) = -1$$

Now, we solve for y:

$$y - 2y - 4 = -1$$
$$-y - 4 = -1$$
$$-y = 3$$
$$y = -3$$

Next, we take the value we just calculated for y and substitute it back into either original equation and solve for x. We will substitute it into equation (2):

$$(2) \qquad x = y + 2$$
$$x = -3 + 2$$
$$x = -1$$

The solution for the system of equations in **Example 1** is the ordered pair (-1,-3).

Sometimes the equations aren't always presented so that one variable is isolated like x was in equation (2) of **Example 1**. We might have this kind of problem:

Example 2. Solve by substitution: (1) $y - 2x = 9$

(2) $y + 3x = -11$

In this situation, you have to first solve for one of the variables. It's like manipulating the formulas in an earlier section. Pick a variable and isolate it on one side of the equation with everything else on the other side. In this example, if we decided to isolate the x on one side we would find that we would have fractions on the other side. While we can do that, it is easier to solve for a variable that has a coefficient of one, in this case y. Since y has a coefficient of one in both equations, we can have our choice of which equation to use. We will choose equation (1).

$$(1) \qquad y - 2x = 9$$
$$y = 2x + 9$$

Now, we take that expression for y and substitute it into equation (2) and solve for x.

$$(2) \qquad y + 3x = -11$$
$$(2x + 9) + 3x = -11$$
$$5x = -20$$
$$x = -4$$

85

(1)　　　$y - 2x = 9$　　　　　Next, substitute this value of x into either

　　　　　$y - 2(-4) = 9$　　　　equation (1) or (2) and solve for y.

　　　　　$y + 8 = 9$

　　　　　$y = 1$

The solution for the system of equations in **Example 2** is the ordered pair (-4,1).

Graphing probably could have solved these first two examples, since we found whole number solutions. Now let's try an example where we have fractional answers. This one really couldn't have been solved accurately by graphing:

Example 3.　　　Solve by substitution:　　(1)　　$x - y = 6$

　　　　　　　　　　　　　　　　(2)　　$2x + 3y = 8$

(1)　　　$x - y = 6$　　　　　First, solve for one of the variables. We will

　　　　　$x = y + 6$　　　　　solve for x in equation (1).

(2)　　　$2x + 3y = 8$　　　　Now, substitute this expression for x into equation (2),

　　　$2(y + 6) + 3y = 8$　　　and solve for y.

　　　$2y + 12 + 3y = 8$

　　　　　　$5y = -4$

　　　　　　$y = -\dfrac{4}{5}$

(1)　　$x - y = 6$　　　　　Next, substitute this value of y into one of the equations and

　　$x - \left(-\dfrac{4}{5}\right) = 6$　　solve for x.

　　　　　$x = \dfrac{26}{5}$　　　The ordered pair is $\left(\dfrac{26}{5}, -\dfrac{4}{5}\right)$

Now try some yourself.

86

Lesson 15: Systems of Equations - The Substitution Method

Exercises

1.   Solve by substitution: (1) $x + y = 8$

                                                          (2) $x = y + 4$

2.   Solve by substitution: (1) $x + y = -7$

                                                           (2) $y = 2x + 2$

3.   Solve by substitution: (1) $x - y = 7$

                                                           (2) $x + 3y = 8$

4.   Solve by substitution: (1) $2x + 3y = 4$

                                                           (2) $2x - y = 8$

Lesson 15: Systems of Equations - The Substitution Method

Solutions

1.   Solve by substitution: (1) $x + y = 8$

(2) $x = y + 4$

Substitute the expression for x given in equation (2) for x in equation (1) and solve for y:

$$(1) \qquad x + y = 8$$
$$(y + 4) + y = 8$$
$$2y = 4$$
$$y = 2$$

Now substitute the value found for y into one of the original equations and solve for x.

$$(2) \qquad x = y + 4$$
$$x = 2 + 4$$
$$x = 6$$

The solution is: (6,2)

2.   Solve by substitution: (1) $x + y = -7$

(2) $y = 2x + 2$

Substitute the expression for y given in equation (2) for y in equation (1) and solve for x:

$$(1) \qquad x + y = -7$$
$$x + (2x + 2) = -7$$
$$3x = -9$$
$$x = -3$$

Now substitute the value found for x into one of the original equations and solve for y.

$$(2) \qquad y = 2x + 2$$
$$y = 2(-3) + 2$$
$$y = -4$$

The solution is: $(-3, -4)$

3.   Solve by substitution: (1) $x - y = 7$

(2) $x + 3y = 8$

Solve for one of the variables in terms of the other. We will solve for x in equation (1).

$$(1) \qquad x - y = 7$$
$$x = y + 7$$

Substitute the expression for x into equation (2) and solve for y.

$$(2) \qquad x + 3y = 8$$
$$(y + 7) + 3y = 8$$
$$4y = 1$$
$$y = \frac{1}{4}$$

Now, substitute the expression for y into one of the original equations and solve for x.

$$(1) \qquad x - y = 7$$
$$x - \frac{1}{4} = 7$$
$$x = \frac{29}{4}$$

The solution is: $\left(\frac{29}{4}, \frac{1}{4} \right)$

4.   Solve by substitution:
$$(1) \qquad 2x + 3y = 4$$
$$(2) \qquad 2x - y = 8$$

No term in either equation has a coefficient of a positive one, but y in equation (2) has a negative one as its coefficient, so we will choose to solve for y in equation (2).

$$(2) \qquad 2x - y = 8$$
$$-y = -2x + 8$$
$$y = 2x - 8$$

Substitute the expression for y into equation (1) and solve for x.

$$(1) \qquad 2x + 3y = 4$$
$$2x + 3(2x - 8) = 4$$
$$2x + 6x - 24 = 4$$
$$8x = 28$$
$$x = \frac{28}{8} = \frac{7}{2}$$

Substitute the expression for x into one of the original equations and solve for y.

$$(2) \qquad 2x - y = 8$$
$$2\left(\frac{7}{2} \right) - y = 8$$
$$7 - y = 8$$
$$y = -1$$

The solution is: $\left(\frac{7}{2}, -1 \right)$

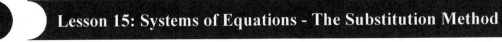

Lesson 15: Systems of Equations - The Substitution Method

Lesson 16: Systems of Equations - The Elimination Method

This is the last of the three methods we will discuss for solving systems of equations. Given a choice in how to solve a system of linear equations in two unknowns, this method is frequently chosen. Let's see why.

Example 1.   Solve by elimination: (1) $2x + 4y = 7$
                                                (2) $3x - 4y = 13$

If we were to use the substitution method, we would have to solve for one of the variables. All the variables in this problem have a coefficient other than one and, hence, we would have fractions involved right from the start, making the work more difficult. For example, if we solved for x in equation (1), we would have:

$$x = \frac{-4y + 7}{2} = -2y + \frac{7}{2}$$

We would then have to substitute that expression into equation (2) and solve for y. It could be done, but there is an easier way – **the elimination method**.

We will use the addition property to help us solve this problem. Remember, the addition property says that we can add anything to one side of the equation as long as we add the same amount to the other side. So, in equation (1), we will add $3x - 4y$ to the left side of the equation and 13 to the right side. Equation (2) says that these are equal amounts. Here's what happens:

(1) $2x + 4y = 7$
(2) $\underline{3x - 4y = 13}$
            $5x = 20$

$$\frac{5x}{5} = \frac{20}{5}$$
$$x = 4$$

When adding equation (2) to equation (1), we add $2x$ and $3x$ and get $5x$. But when we add the y terms ($+4y$ and $-4y$), we get zero, eliminating the y term. The sum of the right sides of the equations yields 20. We now have one equation in one variable that can be easily solved.

(1) $2x + 4y = 7$
        $2 \bullet 4 + 4y = 7$
        $8 + 4y = 7$
        $4y = -1$

$$y = -\frac{1}{4}$$

The solution is: $\left(4, -\frac{1}{4}\right)$

This is only half the answer. We have to find out what y equals. We do that by substituting this x value back into one of the original equations and solving for y.

Naturally, the problem isn't always set up so that by simply adding the two equations, one variable is eliminated. Sometimes, you have to apply the multiplication property first so that a term will be eliminated. Here's an example of how that works.

Example 2.   Solve by elimination: (1) $3x - y = 11$
                                                (2) $5x + 4y = 7$

91

If we added these equations, as they are now, we would not be successful in eliminating either variable. But, if we first apply the multiplication property and multiply equation (1) by 4 and then add the equations, we would successfully eliminate the y terms. Here is the process:

Multiply equation (1) by 4:

$$(4)3x - (4)y = (4)11$$
$$12x - 4y = 44$$

Add equation (2):

$$5x + 4y = 7$$

$$17x = 51$$

Solve for x:

$$x = 3$$

Substitute in equation (1) and solve for y:

$$3(3) - y = 11$$
$$9 - y = 11$$
$$y = -2$$

The solution is: $(3,-2)$

Sometimes, multiplying one equation by a number isn't enough to eliminate a variable. The following example requires two multiplications.

Example 3.   Solve by elimination:

(1) $2x + 4y = 16$

(2) $5x - 3y = 1$

Multiply equation (1) by 3:

And equation (2) by 4:

Add the two equations:

Solve for x:

$$6x + 12y = 48$$
$$20x - 12y = 4$$
$$26x = 52$$
$$x = 2$$

Substitute into equation (1) and solve for y:

$$2(2) + 4y = 16$$
$$4 + 4y = 16$$
$$4y = 12$$
$$y = 3$$

You should find that the elimination method is usually easier to use than the substitution method. Also, if you continue your math career, you may find other opportunities to use the elimination technique.

Now, some practice on the elimination method.

Lesson 16: Systems of Equations - The Elimination Method

Exercises

1.   Solve by elimination: (1) $x + y = 8$

                                                   (2) $-x + y = 6$

2.   Solve by elimination: (1) $3x - 2y = 12$

                                                   (2) $4x + 2y = 2$

3.   Solve by elimination: (1) $5x + 2y = 4$

                                                   (2) $-11x - 6y = 8$

4.   Solve by elimination: (1) $5x - 3y = 10$

                                                   (2) $2x - 6y = 4$

5.   Solve by elimination: (1) $5y = -2x + 9$

                                                   (2) $-6x + 2y = 7$

Lesson 16: Systems of Equations - The Elimination Method

Solutions

1. Solve by elimination:

    (1) $\qquad x + y = 8$
    (2) $\qquad \dfrac{-x + y = 6}{}$

    Add the two equations: $\qquad 2y = 14$
    Solve for y: $\qquad y = 7$
    Substitute into either equation: $\qquad x + 7 = 8$
    Solve for x: $\qquad x = 1$
    Solution is: $\qquad (1, 7)$

2. Solve by elimination:

    (1) $\qquad 3x - 2y = 12$
    (2) $\qquad \dfrac{4x + 2y = 2}{}$

    Add the two equations: $\qquad 7x = 14$
    Solve for x: $\qquad x = 2$
    Substitute into either equation: $\qquad 3(2) - 2y = 12$
    Solve for y: $\qquad 6 - 2y = 12$
    $\qquad -2y = 6$
    $\qquad y = -3$

    Solution is: $\qquad (2, -3)$

3. Solve by elimination:

    (1) $\qquad 5x + 2y = 4$
    (2) $\qquad -11x - 6y = 8$

    Multiply equation (1) by 3: $\qquad 15x + 6y = 12$
    Add result to equation (2): $\qquad \dfrac{-11x - 6y = 8}{}$
    Add these equations: $\qquad 4x = 20$
    Solve for x: $\qquad x = 5$
    Substitute into either equation: $\qquad 5(5) + 2y = 4$
    Solve for y: $\qquad 25 + 2y = 4$
    $\qquad 2y = -21$
    $\qquad y = -\dfrac{21}{2}$

    Solution is: $\qquad \left(5, -\dfrac{21}{2}\right)$

4.   Solve by elimination:

(1) $5x - 3y = 10$
(2) $2x - 6y = 4$

Multiply equation (1) by –2: $-10x + 6y = -20$
Add result to equation (2): $2x - 6y = 4$
$$-8x = -16$$
Solve for x: $x = 2$
Substitute into either equation: $5(2) - 3y = 10$
Solve for y: $10 - 3y = 10$
$$-3y = 0$$
$$y = 0$$

Solution is: $(2,0)$

5.   Solve by elimination:

(1) $5y = -2x + 9$
(2) $-6x + 2y = 7$

Before we can use the multiplication property, we have to put equation (1) in the standard format of $Ax + By = C$. We do this by adding $2x$ to each side, which yields:

(1) $2x + 5y = 9$
Now, multiply equation (1) by 3: $6x + 15y = 27$
Add this to equation (2): $-6x + 2y = 7$
$$17y = 34$$
Solve for y: $y = 2$
Substitute into either equation: $-6x + 2(2) = 7$
Solve for x: $-6x + 4 = 7$
$$-6x = 3$$
$$x = -\frac{1}{2}$$

Solution is: $\left(-\frac{1}{2}, 2\right)$

95

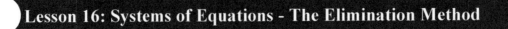

Lesson 16: Systems of Equations - The Elimination Method

Lesson 17: Radicals

From our understanding of exponents, we know that if we multiply a number by itself we get a number squared. For example:

Example 1. $4 \bullet 4 = 4^2 = 16$

We know that 4^2 is 16. Now we are going to look at a number and try to find the number that multiplied by itself yields that number. In other words, we are going to work in reverse from **Example 1**. We will be given the number 16 and asked to find its square root, which is 4. A root is another name for a factor, but it is a specific factor – one that is multiplied by itself. Actually, either positive or negative 4 times itself will equal 16, but we will be dealing with only the positive root.

The way we ask for the square root of a number is to use a radical sign ($\sqrt{}$), with the number placed under the radical sign being called a radicand.

Example 2. $\sqrt{81}$

$\sqrt{81} = 9$

The radicand is 81, and we are looking for the number whose square is 81. Since we have agreed to only use the positive root, the answer is 9, because $9^2 = 81$.

☑ We can check our answer by multiplying, $9 \bullet 9 = 81$

Example 3. $\sqrt{121}$

$\sqrt{121} = 11$

We want to find the square root of 121. What number squared will equal 121?

Example 4. $\sqrt{3^2} = \sqrt{3 \bullet 3} = \sqrt{9} = 3$

In **Example 4**, we have illustrated what happens when we take the square root of a number squared – we get the number itself.

Now let's combine our knowledge of radicals and the operations of multiplication, division, addition and subtraction. We begin with multiplication and the product rule for radicals.

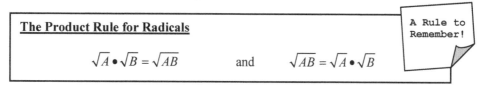

The Product Rule for Radicals

$\sqrt{A} \bullet \sqrt{B} = \sqrt{AB}$ and $\sqrt{AB} = \sqrt{A} \bullet \sqrt{B}$

A Rule to Remember!

We illustrate this rule with a few examples:

Example 5. $\sqrt{3} \bullet \sqrt{7} = \sqrt{21}$ **Example 6.** $\sqrt{55} = \sqrt{11} \bullet \sqrt{5}$

Just as fractions can be simplified so can radical expression sometimes be simplified and we use the product rule to help us do that. Here are some examples:

Example 7. $\sqrt{75}$
$= \sqrt{25} \bullet \sqrt{3}$
$= 5\sqrt{3}$

In this example, we found factors of 75, one of which was a perfect square (25), the other was 3. Then we took the square root of 25, which is 5, and multiplied it times the square root of 3.

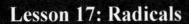

Example 8. $\sqrt{45} = \sqrt{9} \bullet \sqrt{5} = 3\sqrt{5}$

Now let's try some division of radicals. For that, we have a quotient rule for radicals.

> **Quotient Rule for Radicals**
>
> $\dfrac{\sqrt{A}}{\sqrt{B}} = \sqrt{\dfrac{A}{B}}$ and $\sqrt{\dfrac{A}{B}} = \dfrac{\sqrt{A}}{\sqrt{B}}$
>
> A Rule to Remember!

Let's see how that works with some real numbers.

Example 9. $\dfrac{\sqrt{33}}{\sqrt{3}} = \sqrt{\dfrac{33}{3}} = \sqrt{11}$

Example 10. $\sqrt{\dfrac{20}{9}} = \dfrac{\sqrt{20}}{\sqrt{9}} = \dfrac{\sqrt{20}}{3} = \dfrac{\sqrt{4}\sqrt{5}}{3} = \dfrac{2\sqrt{5}}{3}$ This one required some simplification of the numerator.

Now we will tackle addition and subtraction with radicals. For this we will treat the radical like a variable and combine like terms. Just like we can add $2x$ and $3x$ and get $5x$, we can add and subtract the following:

Example 11. $2\sqrt{5} + 3\sqrt{5} = 5\sqrt{5}$

Example 12. $8\sqrt{2} - 5\sqrt{2} = 3\sqrt{2}$

Sometimes we have to simplify some radical expressions before we can combine them.

Example 13. $5\sqrt{18} + 4\sqrt{8}$

In this form it doesn't appear that these radical expressions can be combined. However, if we simplify them first, let's see if that changes the picture.

$$5\sqrt{18} = 5\sqrt{9}\sqrt{2} \qquad\qquad 4\sqrt{8} = 4\sqrt{4}\sqrt{2}$$
$$= 5 \bullet 3\sqrt{2} \qquad\qquad\quad = 4 \bullet 2\sqrt{2}$$
$$= 15\sqrt{2} \qquad\qquad\qquad = 8\sqrt{2}$$

Now each of the terms has been simplified and they both have the same radicand, so they can be combined as follows:

$$15\sqrt{2} + 8\sqrt{2} = 23\sqrt{2}$$

Example 14. $10\sqrt{12} - 2\sqrt{27} = 10\sqrt{4}\sqrt{3} - 2\sqrt{9}\sqrt{3}$
$$= 20\sqrt{3} - 6\sqrt{3}$$
$$= 14\sqrt{3}$$

After simplifying the radicals, they have the same radicand and can be combined.

Your turn. ➡

Lesson 17: Radicals

Exercises

1. Find: $\sqrt{169}$

2. Multiply: $\sqrt{5}\sqrt{7}$

3. Multiply: $\sqrt{3}\sqrt{10}$

4. Simplify: $\sqrt{125}$

5. Simplify: $\sqrt{48}$

6. Simplify: $\dfrac{\sqrt{21}}{\sqrt{3}}$

7. Simplify: $\sqrt{\dfrac{27}{16}}$

8. Add: $3\sqrt{7} + 8\sqrt{7}$

9. Subtract: $16\sqrt{2} - 9\sqrt{2}$

10. Add: $3\sqrt{48} + \sqrt{27}$

Lesson 17: Radicals

Solutions

1. Find: $\sqrt{169} = 13$

2. Multiply: $\sqrt{5}\sqrt{7} = \sqrt{35}$ Use the multiplication rule for radicals.

3. Multiply: $\sqrt{3}\sqrt{10} = \sqrt{30}$ Also, use the multiplication rule.

4. Simplify: $\sqrt{125} = \sqrt{25}\sqrt{5} = 5\sqrt{5}$ Always look for a perfect square factor (4, 9, 16, 25, 49, 64, etc.). In this problem the perfect square factor is 25.

5. Simplify: $\sqrt{48} = \sqrt{16}\sqrt{3} = 4\sqrt{3}$ The perfect square factor here is 16.

6. Simplify: $= \dfrac{\sqrt{21}}{\sqrt{3}} = \sqrt{\dfrac{21}{3}} = \sqrt{7}$ Use the division rule for radicals.

7. Simplify: $\sqrt{\dfrac{27}{16}} = \dfrac{\sqrt{27}}{\sqrt{16}} = \dfrac{\sqrt{9}\sqrt{3}}{4} = \dfrac{3\sqrt{3}}{4}$ Also, use the division rule for this problem.

8. Add: $3\sqrt{7} + 8\sqrt{7} = 11\sqrt{7}$ It's just like combining $3x$ and $8x$ to equal $11x$.

9. Subtract: $16\sqrt{2} - 9\sqrt{2} = 7\sqrt{2}$ Here, it's just like combining $16x$ and $-9x$ to equal $7x$.

10. Add: $3\sqrt{48} + \sqrt{27}$

Simplify the expression first:

$$3\sqrt{48} + \sqrt{27} = 3\sqrt{16}\sqrt{3} + \sqrt{9}\sqrt{3}$$
$$= 3 \bullet 4\sqrt{3} + 3\sqrt{3}$$
$$= 12\sqrt{3} + 3\sqrt{3} = 15\sqrt{3}$$

After simplifying the expression, then combine like terms (terms with the same radicand).

Lesson 18: The Pythagorean Theorem

We can use our knowledge of radicals to help solve problems dealing with right triangles based on the relationship between the lengths of the sides. This relationship is called the **Pythagorean Theorem** and is named after Pythagoras, a Greek mathematician who lived about 2500 years ago! Can you believe folks who lived that long ago were that smart?!

> **A Rule to Remember!**
>
> **The Pythagorean Theorem**
>
> In a right triangle, the square of the length of the hypotenuse (longest side of the triangle, c) is equal to the sum of the squares of the lengths of the legs of the triangle (a and b). It looks like this:
>
> $$c^2 = a^2 + b^2$$

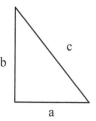

With this formula, if we are given the length of any two sides of a right triangle, we can find the length of the third side. Here are a few examples:

Example 1.

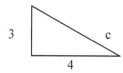

$c^2 = 3^2 + 4^2$ Using this information, this is what the equation looks like.
$c^2 = 9 + 16$
$c^2 = 25$ This says that in a right triangle, with sides of 3 units and 4 units, the
$c = 5$ hypotenuse is 5 units.

Example 2.

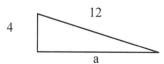

$12^2 = a^2 + 4^2$ In this example, we know the hypotenuse and one of the legs, so the
$144 = a^2 + 16$ equation sets up like this.
$144 - 16 = a^2$
$128 = a^2$

$$a = \sqrt{128} = \sqrt{64}\sqrt{2} = 8\sqrt{2}$$

This represents the exact answer to the problem. The unknown leg of the triangle, a, equals: $8\sqrt{2}$

If we wanted to get an approximate answer, we could use our calculator to determine what the square root of 128 is. We say an approximate answer, because the square root of 128 is a decimal number with a never-ending decimal. So, we would generally round the answer to a few decimal places. For this example let's round to three decimal places.

$$\sqrt{128} = 11.313708 = 11.314$$

Example 3. Find the unknown leg and round to two decimal places.

$$15^2 = 5^2 + b^2$$
$$225 = 25 + b^2$$
$$200 = b^2$$

$$b = \sqrt{200} = \sqrt{100}\sqrt{2} = 10\sqrt{2}$$
$$\sqrt{200} = 14.142135 = 14.14$$

The exact answer is $\sqrt{200}$ or, in it's simplified form $10\sqrt{2}$, and the approximate answer rounded to two decimal places is 14.14.

Now try some of these problems of Pythagoras!

Lesson 18: The Pythagorean Theorem

Exercises

Find the length of the side not given. Find the exact answer and an approximate answer to two decimal places:

    1. $a = 5, b = 8$

    2. $a = 12, c = 15$

    3. $b = 6, c = 14$

    4. $a = 7, b = 8$

    5. $a = 4, c = 15$

    6. $b = 2, c = 8$

Solutions

Find the length of the side not given. Find the exact answer and an approximate answer to two decimal places:

1. $a = 5$, $b = 8$
   The equation sets up like this:
   $$c^2 = 5^2 + 8^2$$
   $$c^2 = 25 + 64$$
   $$c^2 = 89$$
   Exact answer: $\quad c = \sqrt{89}$
   Approximate answer: $\quad c = 9.43$

2. $a = 12$, $c = 15$
   The equation sets up like this:
   $$15^2 = 12^2 + b^2$$
   $$225 = 144 + b^2$$
   $$81 = b^2$$
   Exact and approximate answer: $\quad 9 = b$

3. $b = 6$, $c = 14$
   The equation sets up like this:
   $$14^2 = a^2 + 6^2$$
   $$196 = a^2 + 36$$
   $$160 = a^2$$
   Exact answer: $\quad a = \sqrt{160} = \sqrt{16}\sqrt{10} = 4\sqrt{10}$
   Approximate answer: $\quad a = 12.65$

4. $a = 7$, $b = 8$
   The equation sets up like this:
   $$c^2 = 7^2 + 8^2$$
   $$c^2 = 49 + 64$$
   $$c^2 = 113$$
   Exact answer: $\quad c = \sqrt{113}$
   Approximate answer: $\quad c = 10.63$

5. $a = 4$, $c = 15$
   The equation sets up like this:
   $$15^2 = 4^2 + b^2$$
   $$225 = 16 + b^2$$
   $$209 = b^2$$
   Exact answer: $\quad b = \sqrt{209}$
   Approximate answer: $\quad b = 14.46$

6. $b = 2$, $c = 8$
   The equation sets up like this:
   $$8^2 = a^2 + 2^2$$
   $$64 = a^2 + 4$$
   $$60 = a^2$$
   Exact answer: $\quad a = \sqrt{60} = 2\sqrt{15}$
   Approximate answer: $\quad a = 7.75$

Lesson 19: The Quadratic Formula

Earlier in this course, when we had a quadratic equation, we solved it using the principle of zero products. That is, we factored the quadratic expression and set each factor equal to zero and solved those equations. Remember, it went like this:

Example 1. Solve: $x^2 + 4x + 3 = 0$

$$(x+3)(x+1) = 0$$

$$x + 3 = 0 \qquad x + 1 = 0$$
$$x = -3 \qquad x = -1$$

This method works fine if the quadratic expression is factorable. But what happens if the quadratic expression is not factorable or the factors are difficult to find? The method we use then is the *quadratic formula*. Taking the standard form of a quadratic expression and solving for x yields the quadratic formula.

Standard Form	**The Quadratic Formula**
$$ax^2 + bx + c = 0$$ If we solve this for x, we get the quadratic formula.	*A Rule to Remember!* $$x = \frac{-b \pm \sqrt{b^2 - 4ac}}{2a}$$

Before we can use the quadratic formula, we need to always make sure the quadratic equation is in standard form so we can properly identify the a, b, and c values.

Example 2. Identify the a, b, and c values of $3x^2 + 5x - 10 = 0$

$$\underset{a}{3x^2} + \underset{b}{5x} - \underset{c}{10}$$

$a = 3$
$b = 5$
$c = -10$

Example 3. Identify the a, b, and c values of $2x^2 = 6x + 9$
First, put the equation in standard form: $2x^2 - 6x - 9 = 0$

$a = 2 \qquad\qquad b = -6 \qquad\qquad c = -9$

Now, let's try an example and solve for x using the quadratic formula.

Example 4. Solve: $2x^2 - 7x - 15 = 0$

First, identify the a, b, and c values:
$a = 2$
$b = -7$
$c = -15$

Then substitute these values into the quadratic formula.

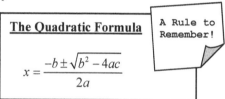

$$x = \frac{-(-7) \pm \sqrt{(-7)^2 - 4(2)(-15)}}{2(2)}$$

$$= \frac{7 \pm \sqrt{49 + 120}}{4}$$

$$= \frac{7 \pm \sqrt{169}}{4} = \frac{7 \pm 13}{4}$$

Since a quadratic equation yields two solutions, our two solutions for this example are:

$$x = \frac{7+13}{4} = \frac{20}{4} = 5 \qquad \text{and} \qquad x = \frac{7-13}{4} = \frac{-6}{4} = -\frac{3}{2}$$

Did you recognize that this example could have been solved by factoring?

$$\text{The factors are: } (x-5)(2x+3)$$

Setting each factor equal to zero and solving gives us the same answers. Here is another example.

Example 5.   Solve: $3x^2 - 8x - 2 = 0$

$a = 3, \quad b = \text{-8}, \quad c = \text{-2}$

$$x = \frac{-(-8) \pm \sqrt{(-8)^2 - 4(3)(-2)}}{2(3)}$$

$$= \frac{8 \pm \sqrt{64 + 24}}{6}$$

$$= \frac{8 \pm \sqrt{88}}{6}$$

$$= \frac{8 \pm \sqrt{4}\sqrt{22}}{6}$$

$$= \frac{8 \pm 2\sqrt{22}}{6}$$

Simplify these fractions by finding a common factor of 2 in the numerator and denominator.

$$= \frac{2(4 \pm \sqrt{22})}{2 \bullet 3}$$

The solution is: $x = \dfrac{4 + \sqrt{22}}{3}$ and $x = \dfrac{4 - \sqrt{22}}{3}$

Let's try one more.

Example 6.   Solve: $4x^2 = 9x + 3$

$\qquad\qquad 4x^2 - 9x - 3 = 0$ First put in standard form.

$\qquad\qquad a = 4, \quad b = \text{-9}, \quad c = \text{-3}$ Identify the a, b, and c values.

$$x = \frac{-(-9) \pm \sqrt{(-9)^2 - 4(4)(-3)}}{2(4)}$$ Substitute in the quadratic formula.

$$= \frac{9 \pm \sqrt{81 + 48}}{8}$$

$$= \frac{9 \pm \sqrt{129}}{8}$$

$$x = \frac{9 + \sqrt{129}}{8} \quad \text{and} \quad x = \frac{9 - \sqrt{129}}{8}$$

It is perfectly acceptable to leave the answer with a $\pm$ rather than write two answers, one with a plus sign and one with a minus sign.

106

Lesson 19: The Quadratic Formula

Exercises: Solve.

1. $x^2 + 7x + 12 = 0$

2. $3x^2 - 10 = 13x$

3. $2x^2 - 5x - 8 = 0$

4. $5x^2 + 8x - 2 = 0$

5. $4x^2 - 5 = -4x$

Lesson 19: The Quadratic Formula

Solutions

1. Solve using the quadratic formula: $x^2 + 7x + 12 = 0$
   Identify the a, b, and c values: $a = 1,\ b = 7,\ c = 12$

   Substitute in the quadratic formula: $x = \dfrac{-7 \pm \sqrt{49 - 4(1)(12)}}{2(1)}$

   Solve for x:
   $$= \dfrac{-7 \pm \sqrt{49 - 48}}{2}$$
   $$= \dfrac{-7 \pm 1}{2}$$

   Solutions are: $x = -4$ and $x = -3$

2. Solve using the quadratic formula: $3x^2 - 10 = 13x$
   First put in the standard format: $3x^2 - 13x - 10 = 0$
   Identify the a, b, and c values: $a = 3,\ b = -13,\ c = -10$

   Substitute in the quadratic formula: $x = \dfrac{-(-13) \pm \sqrt{(-13)^2 - 4(3)(-10)}}{2(3)}$

   Solve for x:
   $$= \dfrac{13 \pm \sqrt{169 + 120}}{6}$$
   $$= \dfrac{13 \pm \sqrt{289}}{6} = \dfrac{13 \pm 17}{6}$$

   Solutions are: $x = 5$ and $x = -\dfrac{2}{3}$

3. Solve: $2x^2 - 5x - 8 = 0$
   Identify the a, b, and c values: $a = 2,\ b = -5,\ c = -8$

   Substitute in the quadratic formula: $x = \dfrac{-(-5) \pm \sqrt{(-5)^2 - 4(2)(-8)}}{2(2)}$

   Solve for x:
   $$= \dfrac{5 \pm \sqrt{25 + 64}}{4}$$

   Solutions are:
   $$= \dfrac{5 \pm \sqrt{89}}{4}$$

4. Solve: $5x^2 + 8x - 2 = 0$
   Identify the a, b, and c values: $a = 5,\ b = 8,\ c = -2$

   Substitute in the quadratic formula: $x = \dfrac{-8 \pm \sqrt{8^2 - 4(5)(-2)}}{2(5)}$

   Solve for x:
   $$= \dfrac{-8 \pm \sqrt{64 + 40}}{10}$$
   $$= \dfrac{-8 \pm \sqrt{104}}{10} = \dfrac{-8 \pm \sqrt{4}\sqrt{26}}{10} = \dfrac{-8 \pm 2\sqrt{26}}{10}$$

   Simplifying, the solutions are:
   $$= \dfrac{-4 \pm \sqrt{26}}{5}$$

5. Solve: $4x^2 - 5 = -4x$
   First put in standard form: $4x^2 + 4x - 5 = 0$
   Identify the a, b, and c values: $a = 4,\ b = 4,\ c = -5$
   Substitute in the quadratic formula:
   $$x = \dfrac{-4 \pm \sqrt{4^2 - 4(4)(-5)}}{2(4)}$$

   Solve for x:
   $$= \dfrac{-4 \pm \sqrt{16 + 80}}{8} = \dfrac{-4 \pm \sqrt{96}}{8} = \dfrac{-4 \pm \sqrt{16}\sqrt{6}}{8}$$

   Solutions are:
   $$= \dfrac{-4 \pm 4\sqrt{6}}{8} = \dfrac{-1 \pm \sqrt{6}}{2}$$

Lesson 20: Word Problems

Why do we emphasize word problems? Well, you don't get many opportunities to solve an equation at the grocery store, or add fractions at the gas station. But, you do have to figure out how much paint you need to paint your walls or how much fertilizer to buy for your lawn or how much sales tax you will pay. And even if you don't run into real life opportunities to use the math you learn here, mathematics is about logic and helping you to think logically. So, learning how to approach word problems will help you to think logically.

The word problems discussed here will emphasize concepts learned in the second half of this course. But the process is basically the same as used in the first section on word problems. So you don't have to leaf back through the book to review the process, we repeat it here.

Step 1: Understand the problem. One of the best ways to understand a word problem is to try to draw a picture that represents the problem. It may not always be possible, but be creative and find some way to represent the problem in a drawing. The drawing helps give you an idea of what might be a <u>reasonable</u> answer for the problem. All too often, students do a calculation that results in an impossible or at least unreasonable answer to the problem. After you understand the problem, write the English sentence to be translated. Use variables to represent unknown quantities.

Step 2: Translate. Translate the known information into an algebraic equation.

Step 3: Solve the equation. Use the steps for solving equations learned earlier in this course to solve the equation(s).

Step 4: Solve the problem! Sometimes the solution to the equation only gets you part way to the answer to the problem. So, check the wording of the problem and make sure you provide the answer to the question the problem poses – and don't forget to include the proper units for the answer (feet, inches, pounds, etc.).

Step 5: Check to see if your answer is reasonable based on your understanding of the problem.

Let's start with an example where a drawing is easy.

> **Example 1.** A 14-foot ladder is leaning against a house. The bottom of the ladder is 6 feet from the house. How high is the top of the ladder? Round the answer to the nearest tenth of a foot.

Step 1: Understand the problem. (Draw a picture)

You should recognize that this problem involves a right triangle and therefore, requires use of the Pythagorean Theorem to solve it. The Pythagorean Theorem says that, $a^2 + b^2 = c^2$.

We know one of the legs of the triangle and the hypotenuse, so we can proceed to step 2.

Step 2: Translate. $\qquad 6^2 + b^2 = 14^2$

Step 3: Solve the equation. $\qquad 36 + b^2 = 196$
$$b^2 = 196 - 36$$
$$b^2 = 160$$
$$b = \sqrt{160}$$

Use your calculator to find the square root of 160.

Step 4: Solve the problem. $\qquad b = 12.64911$

Lesson 20: Word Problems

Look at the problem again and you will see that the answer is to be rounded to the nearest tenth, so our final answer is that the top of the ladder is 12.6 ft high. Part of this step is to make sure we include the proper units, which in this case are feet.

Step 5: Check.

$$6^2 + (\sqrt{160})^2 = 14^2$$
$$36 + 160 = 196$$
$$196 = 196$$

Example 2. Two families went to the movies. The first family had 2 adults and 2 children and they paid $26. The second family had three adults (Gramma tagged along) and four children and they paid $44. How much was an adult ticket and how much was a child's ticket?

Step 1: Understand the problem. A picture may not help with this one, but you still need to make sure you understand the problem. There are two things the problem asks us to find out and they are the price of an adult ticket and the price of a child's ticket. So we have two unknowns and therefore we need two equations. With two equations, we can set up a system of equations and then solve them by substitution or elimination.

Let a = cost of an adult ticket and let c = cost of a child's ticket

Step 2: Translate. Translate the known information to two equations. In the first equation, we multiply the number of adult tickets by 2 and the number of children's tickets by 2 and the result is 26. In the second equation, we multiply the number of adult tickets by 3 and the number of children's tickets by 4 and the result is 44. The two equations are:

$$2a + 2c = 26 \qquad\qquad 3a + 4c = 44$$

Step 3: Solve the equations. Let's solve this by elimination by multiplying the first equation by –2, and then adding the two equations:

$$-4a - 4c = -52$$
$$\underline{3a + 4c = 44}$$
$$-a = -8$$
$$a = 8$$

Step 4: Solve the problem. This means that an adult ticket cost $8. To find out the price of a child's ticket, we have to substitute the value for an adult ticket back into one of the original equations, as follows.

$$2(8) + 2c = 26$$
$$16 + 2c = 26$$
$$2c = 10$$
$$c = 5$$

So, the answer to this example is an adult ticket costs $8 and a child's ticket costs $5.

Step 5: Check.

$$2(8) + 2(5) = 26$$
$$16 + 10 = 26$$

110

Lesson 20: Word Problems

Example 3. The length of a rectangle is 4 yards less than twice the width. The area is 240 sq. yds. Find the length and the width.

Step 1: Understand the problem (draw a picture).

Remember that the formula for area is length times width.

$$2x - 4$$

x | $A = 240 yd^2$

Step 2: Translate. Substitute our known quantities into the formula for area, as follows:

$$A = l \bullet w$$
$$240 = (2x - 4)x$$
$$240 = 2x^2 - 4x$$
$$2x^2 - 4x - 240 = 0$$

Since this is a quadratic equation, we must put in standard form. We may now either factor or use the quadratic formula.

Step 3: Solve the equation. $\quad 2(x - 12)(x + 10) = 0$

Using the principle of zero products, the two possible solutions are 12 and –10.

Step 4: Solve the Problem. Since a distance can never be negative, the only valid answer is 12. Substitute 12 back into the original representation for the length $(2x - 4)$ and we get a length of 20. So we can state our answers as:

Length = 20 yds. Width = 12 yds.

Step 5: Check. $\quad A = l \bullet w$
$\quad\quad\quad\quad\quad A = 20 \bullet 12$
$\quad\quad\quad\quad\quad A = 240$

Now, some final problems!!

Lesson 20: Word Problems

Lesson 20: Word Problems

Exercises

1. A 12-foot ladder leans against a building. The base of the ladder is 4 feet from the building. How high does the ladder reach? Round to the nearest tenth of a foot.

2. Suppose 750 tickets are sold for a Montgomery College football game for total revenue of $3375. If regular tickets cost $5.50 and student tickets cost $3.00, how many of each kind of tickets were sold?

3. The length of a rectangular garden is 6 meters greater than the width. The area of the rectangle is 135 square meters. Find the length and width of the rectangle.

Lesson 20: Word Problems

Solutions

1. A 12 foot ladder leans against a building. The base of the ladder is 4 feet from the building. How high does the ladder reach? Round to the nearest tenth of a foot.

Step 1: Understand the problem (draw a picture).

Step 2: Translate. This problem involves a right triangle so we should use the Pythagorean theorem to solve it.

$$a^2 + b^2 = c^2$$
$$x^2 + 4^2 = 12^2$$

Step 3: Solve the equation.

$$x^2 + 16 = 144$$
$$x^2 = 128$$
$$x = \sqrt{128} = 11.3137085$$

Step 4: Solve the problem. Round to the nearest tenth of a foot. $x = 11.3$ ft

Step 5: Check. Can you check the answer?

2. Suppose 750 tickets are sold for a Montgomery College football game for total revenue of $3375. If regular tickets cost $5.50 and student tickets cost $3.00, how many of each kind of tickets were sold?

Step 1: Understand the problem. This problem involves two unknown quantities – the number of regular tickets sold (r) and the number of student tickets sold (s). We need to develop two equations using these unknown quantities and then solve by substitution or elimination. One of the equations will be a cost equation and one will be a quantity equation.

Step 2: Translate. The quantity equation will show that the number of regular tickets sold plus the number of student tickets sold will equal the total attendance of 750:

$$r + s = 750$$

The cost equation will multiply the number of each type of ticket sold by the price of that ticket and the sum of those two quantities will be the total revenue for the game:

$$5.50r + 3s = 3375$$

Step 3: Solve the equations.

$$r + s = 750$$
$$5.50r + 3s = 3375$$

Solve by elimination (multiply the first equation by –3, then add the two equations):

$$-3r - 3s = -2250$$
$$\underline{5.50r + 3s = 3375}$$
$$2.5r = 1125$$
$$r = 450$$

Step 4: Solve the problem. The number of regular tickets sold was 450, so substitute that number back into either equation to find the number of student tickets.

The solution is: 450 regular tickets and 300 student tickets

Step 5: Check. $450 + 300 = 750$

3. The length of a rectangular garden is 6 meters greater than the width. The area of the rectangle is 135 meters squared. Find the length and width of the rectangle.

Step1: Understand the problem (draw a picture).

x | $A = 135m^2$

$x + 6$

Since this problem deals with area, we have to use the formula for the area of a rectangle to solve it.

Step 2: Translate. Set up the formula for the area of a rectangle and substitute the known quantities.

$$A = l \bullet w$$
$$135 = (x + 6)x$$

Step 3: Solve the equation:

$$135 = x^2 + 6x$$
$$x^2 + 6x - 135 = 0$$
$$(x + 15)(x - 9) = 0$$
$$x = -15 \quad \text{and} \quad x = 9$$

Step 4: Solve the problem. As we saw in the first problem, distance can not be negative, so we use the positive result of $x = 9$ which represents the width. Substitute that value back into the expression that represents the length and we find that the answer is:

Width = 9 meters
Length = 15 meters

Step 5: Check.

$$A = l \bullet w$$
$$A = 9 \bullet 15 = 135$$

Now try the practice test for elementary algebra!

Lesson 20: Word Problems

1. Simplify the expression. Do not use negative exponents in your answer.

   $(3x^{-4}y^3)^3$ Answer: _____

2. Simplify the expression. Do not use negative exponents in your answer.

   $\dfrac{x^4 y^3}{x^{-2} y^4}$ Answer: _____

3. Evaluate: $x^3 - 5x^2 + x + x^0$ when $x = -2$ Answer: _____

4. Solve: $3x - 10 = 2x - 6(x - 3)$ Answer: _____

5. Find the equation of the line that contains the points (1, -5) and (-2, -14):

   Answer: _____

6. Solve: $x^2 = 7x - 12$ Answer: _____

7. Solve: $5x^2 - 3x = 0$ Answer: _____

8. Solve using the quadratic formula: $3x^2 - 5x - 3 = 0$ Answer: _____

9. Solve: $1 + 5x \le 8x - 11$ Answer: _____

10. Solve the system of equations: (1) $2x + 3y = 11$
                                          (2) $4x - 5y = -33$ Answer: _____

21 – Elementary Algebra Practice Test

11.   Solve for m: $f = \dfrac{kMm}{d^2}$ Answer: _____

12.   Multiply: $(2x - 7)^2$ Answer: _____

13.   Factor completely: $3x^3 - 9x^2 - 30x$ Answer: _____

14.   Factor completely: $9x^2 - 64$ Answer: _____

15.   Graph using intercepts: $3x + 2y = 12$

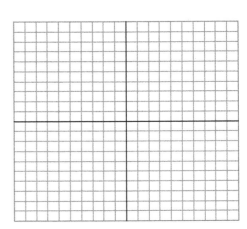

16.   Add and simplify, if possible: $\dfrac{5}{2x^2 y} + \dfrac{4}{3xy^2}$

                                                          Answer: _____

17.   Divide and simplify, if possible: $\dfrac{x^2 - 1}{4x + 4} \div \dfrac{2x^2 - 4x + 2}{8x + 8}$

                                                          Answer: _____

18.   Determine the slope and y-intercept: $5x - 3y = 6$

                                                          Slope: _____

y-intercept: _____

19. The width of a rectangle is 5 meters less then the length. The area is 36 square meters. Find the length and width. Set up an equation and solve.

Length: _____
Width: _____

20. The circus is in town. Admission for 3 adults and 4 children is $30, while the admission for 2 adults and 5 children is $28.75. What is the price of each type of ticket?

Adult ticket: _____
Children's ticket: _____

21 – Elementary Algebra Practice Test

Answers to Algebra Practice Test

1. Simplify the expression. Do not use negative exponents in your answer.

    $$(3x^{-4}y^3)^3$$
    Answer: $\dfrac{27y^9}{x^{12}}$

    See exercise problem # 8 in Rules for Exponents lesson.

2. Simplify the expression. Do not use negative exponents in your answer.

    $$\dfrac{x^4y^3}{x^{-2}y^4}$$
    Answer: $\dfrac{x^6}{y}$

    See exercise problem # 4 in Rules for Exponents lesson.

3. Evaluate: $x^3 - 5x^2 + x + x^0$ when $x = -2$ \qquad Answer: -29

    See exercise problem # 10 in Rules for Exponents lesson.

4. Solve: $3x - 10 = 2x - 6(x - 3)$ \qquad Answer: $x = 4$

    See exercise problem #4 in Solving Equations: Using Both Properties lesson.

5. Find the equation of the line that contains the points (1, -5) and (-2, -14):

    Answer: $y = 3x - 8$

    See exercise problem #7 in More on Graphing lesson.

6. Solve: $x^2 = 7x - 12$ \qquad Answer: $x = 3, 4$

    See exercise problem #7 in Solving Quadratic Equations by Factoring lesson.

7. Solve: $5x^2 - 3x = 0$ \qquad Answer: $x = 0, \dfrac{3}{5}$

    See exercise problem #1 in Solving Quadratic Equations by Factoring lesson.

8. Solve using the quadratic formula: $3x^2 - 5x - 3 = 0$ \qquad Answer: $x = \dfrac{5 \pm \sqrt{61}}{6}$

    See exercise problem # 4 in The Quadratic Formula lesson.

9. Solve: $1 + 5x \le 8x - 11$ \qquad Answer: $x \ge 4$

    See exercise problem # 4 in the Solving Inequalities lesson.

10. Solve the system of equations: \qquad (1) $2x + 3y = 11$

    \qquad (2) $4x - 5y = -33$ \qquad Answer: $(-2, 5)$

    See exercise problem # 4 in the Systems of Equations: The Elimination Method lesson.

11. Solve for m: $\qquad f = \dfrac{kMm}{d^2}$ $\qquad$ Answer: $m = \dfrac{fd^2}{kM}$

See exercise problem # 3 in the Working with Formulas lesson.

12. Simplify: $\qquad (2x-7)^2$ $\qquad$ Answer: $4x^2 - 28x + 49$

See Examples in the Special Products of Binomials lesson.

13. Factor completely: $\qquad 3x^3 - 9x^2 - 30x$ $\qquad$ Answer: $3x(x-5)(x+2)$

See exercise problem # 9 in the Introduction to Factoring lesson.

14. Factor completely: $\qquad 9x^2 - 64$ $\qquad$ Answer: $(3x-8)(3x+8)$

See exercise problem # 2 in the Factoring Squares lesson.

15. Graph using intercepts: $3x + 2y = 12$

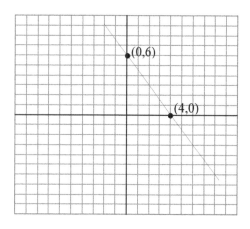

See Example 1 in the lesson on Graphing

16. Add and simplify, if possible: $\qquad \dfrac{5}{2x^2 y} + \dfrac{4}{3xy^2}$

$\qquad\qquad\qquad$ Answer: $\dfrac{15y + 8x}{6x^2 y^2}$

See exercise problem # 7 in the Rational Expressions: Add & Subtract lesson.

17. Divide and simplify, if possible: $\qquad \dfrac{x^2 - 1}{4x+4} \div \dfrac{2x^2 - 4x + 2}{8x + 8}$

$\qquad\qquad\qquad$ Answer: $\dfrac{x+1}{x-1}$

See exercise problem # 10 in the Rational Expressions: Division lesson.

18. Determine the slope and y-intercept: $5x - 3y = 6$ $\qquad$ Slope: $\dfrac{5}{3}$

_y_-intercept: (0, −2)

See exercise problem # 3 in the More on Graphing lesson.

19.   The width of a rectangle is 5 meters less then the length. The area is 36 square meters. Find the length and width. Set up an equation and solve.

Length: 9 meters

Width: 4 meters

See exercise problem # 3 in the More Word Problems lesson.

20.   The circus is in town. Admission for 3 adults and 4 children is $30, while the admission for 2 adults and 5 children is $28.75. What is the price of each type of ticket?

Adult ticket: $5.00

Children's ticket: $3.75

See Example 2 in the More Word Problems lesson.

Lesson 22: Functions and Relations

We start the review of Intermediate Algebra with the basics of linear functions. To understand linear functions we need to define some words. The words are *relation* and *function*. Let's first look at the word *relation*. We have seen examples of relations in the Elementary Algebra lessons when we discussed ordered pairs. An ordered pair shows a relation between x and y values. A linear equation in two variables is an infinite set of relations between x and y values. We can see a few of these relations in the table below for the linear equation $y = x + 3$:

x	y
0	3
1	4
2	5
3	6

One way to think about a relation is that it is a machine that turns an input into an output where the x value is the input and the y value is the output.

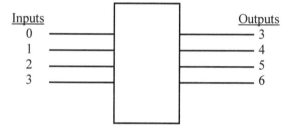

Now let's discuss the concept of *function*. We use this term to describe a relationship between two things. For example, we say that the amount of water in our reservoirs is *a function of* the amount of rain that falls. Or, we might say the time it takes to get to a particular location is *a function of* the speed with which we travel. In a mathematical function, one input has to yield **exactly** one output. Now let's look at some examples.

Example 1. Is this relation a function?

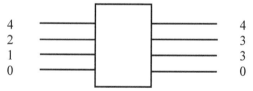

This relation is a function because <u>each input goes to one output</u>. It's OK for that *output* to be the same value as another *output*.

Example 2. Are these relations functions?

Relation 1			Relation 2	
x	y_1		x	y_2
1	3		7	1
2	5		11	2
3	7		13	3
3	9		15	4

Relation 1 is not a function because the input 3 doesn't know where to go: to 7 or 9. Relation 2 is a function, since our input-output machine knows where to send each input.

Example 3. Is $y = \pm x$ a function? If we substitute $x = 2$, we get two values for y, 2 and -2. So our machine that turns inputs into outputs doesn't know where to send the input value. Therefore, this is not a function.

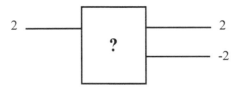

Example 4. Is $y = x^2$ a function? An x value of 2 results in a y value of 4. Also an x value of –2 results in a y value of 4. It is OK to have two different inputs go to the same output but not the other way around. So, this is a function.

A good way to tell if an equation is a function is to think of the input-output machine. Can the machine tell what to do with the input? If it has two or more choices as to where to send the input then it isn't a function.

Vertical Line Test

| A Rule to Remember! | Another way to tell if an equation is a function is to look at its graph. If a vertical line intersects the graph at more than one point than it is not a function. This **vertical line test** helps to show that any linear equation is a function except the type $x = c$ where c is a constant since this represents a vertical line itself. Let's look at some graphs and use the vertical line test on them. Are the following graphs functions? |

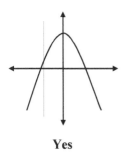

Yes

Passes the vertical line test. There is no vertical line that would intersect this graph in more than one place.

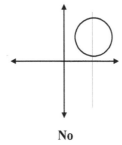

No

A vertical line could intersect this graph in two points.

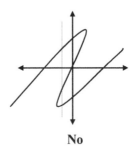

No

A vertical line could intersect this graph in as many as three points

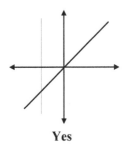

Yes

The last graph is a non-vertical line. As noted above any non-vertical line is a function.

Now it's your turn.

Lesson 22: Functions and Relations

Exercises

1. Are these relations functions?

Relation 1		Relation 2		Relation 3		Relation 4		Relation 5	
x	y_1	x	y_2	x	y_3	x	y_4	x	y_5
0	4	3	3	4	2	1	8	1	1
1	3	2	3	4	1	3	11	−1	1
2	2	1	3	4	0	5	17	2	4
3	1	0	3	4	−1	5	26	−2	4

2. Determine whether the following graphs are functions.

a. 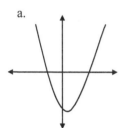   b. 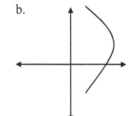   c. 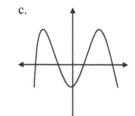   d.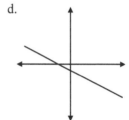

Lesson 22: Functions and Relations

Solutions

1. Are these relations functions?

Relation 1		Relation 2		Relation 3		Relation 4		Relation 5	
x	y_1	x	y_2	x	y_3	x	y_4	x	y_5
0	4	3	3	4	2	1	8	1	1
1	3	2	3	4	1	3	11	−1	1
2	2	1	3	4	0	5	17	2	4
3	1	0	3	4	−1	5	26	−2	4

Relation 1 *is a function* because each input corresponds to exactly one output.

Relation 2 *is a function* because each input corresponds to exactly one output – even though each output is the same. The input output machine knows where to send each input.

Relation 3 *is not a function* because the input output machine doesn't know where to send each input. In the table shown, the input 4 goes to 4 *different* places.

Relation 4 *is not a function* because the input 5 goes to two different outputs.

Relation 5 *is a function* also because each input corresponds to exactly one output.

2. Determine whether the following graphs are functions.

a. 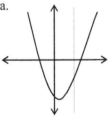　　b. 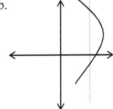　　c. 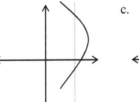　　d.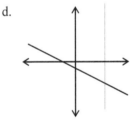

　　Function　　　　　Not a function　　　　Function　　　　　Function

Only graph b fails the vertical line test and is, therefore, not a function. The others are all functions.

126

Lesson 23: Function Notation

Now, let's look at function notation. In the equation $y = x + 3$, note that the value of y depends on the value of x. We assign a value to x and calculate the value of y. So, we call y the *dependent variable* and x the *independent variable*. We say that y is a function of x. We could write it like this:

> $y = f(x)$ and we would say "y is a function of x".

So, instead of $y = x + 3$, we would write it like this: $f(x) = x + 3$. This is function notation. The most common function notation is $f(x)$, but other letters may be used instead of f. Other common symbols are $g(x)$ and $h(x)$.

Using function notation, we could say for the function $f(x) = x + 3$ "find $f(5)$". This means we want to find the value of the function when $x = 5$. Substituting $x = 5$ into the equation, we find:

$$f(5) = 5 + 3 = 8$$

Example 1. Let $f(x) = -3x + 7$ and find $f(2)$.

$$f(2) = -3(2) + 7 \quad \text{Substitute the value of 2 for } x.$$
$$f(2) = 1$$

Example 2. Find $f(a)$ for the function in **Example 1**.

$$f(a) = -3(a) + 7 \quad \text{Substitute the value of } a \text{ for } x.$$
$$f(a) = -3a + 7$$

Example 3. Find $f(a+4)$ for the function in **Example 1**.

$$f(a+4) = -3(a+4) + 7 \quad \text{Substitute the value of } a + 4 \text{ for } x.$$
$$f(a+4) = -3a - 12 + 7$$
$$f(a+4) = -3a - 5$$

We can also be asked to find the value of x given the value of the function.

Example 4. Let $f(x) = 2x - 5$ For what value of x is $f(x) = 15$?

In this case, we set the function equal to 15 and solve for x.

$$15 = 2x - 5 \quad \text{Substitute the value of 15 for } f(x) \text{ and solve for } x.$$
$$20 = 2x$$
$$10 = x$$

127

Example 5. For what value of x is $f(x) = a$ for the function in **Example 4**?

$a = 2x - 5$ Substitute the value of a for $f(x)$

$a + 5 = 2x$ and solve for x.

$\dfrac{a+5}{2} = x$

We can also combine functions as in the next example:

Example 6. Let $f(x) = 3x + 4$ and $g(x) = 2x - 9$ Find: $f(x) + g(x)$

In this case, we add the two functions together and combine like terms:

$f(x) + g(x) = (3x + 4) + (2x - 9)$ Add the two functions.

$f(x) + g(x) = 5x - 5$

Example 7. Find $f(x) - g(x)$ for the functions in **Example 6**.

$f(x) - g(x) = (3x + 4) - (2x - 9)$ Subtract the second function

$f(x) - g(x) = 3x + 4 - 2x + 9$ from the first function.

$f(x) - g(x) = x + 13$

Example 8. Find $2f(x) + 3g(x)$ for the functions in **Example 6**.

$2f(x) + 3g(x) = 2(3x + 4) + 3(2x - 9)$ Twice $f(x)$ plus 3 times $g(x)$.

$2f(x) + 3g(x) = 6x + 8 + 6x - 27$

$2f(x) + 3g(x) = 12x - 19$

Now try some exercises.

Lesson 23: Function Notation

Exercises

1. Let $f(x) = x + 4$ and $g(x) = 2x - 3$

   a. Find $f(x) + g(x)$ d. Find $f(a) + g(a)$

   b. Find $f(x) - g(x)$ e. For what value of x is $f(x) = 5$?

   c. Find $f(2) + g(-2)$ f. For what value of x is $g(x) = 17$?

2. Let $f(x) = 2x - 5$ and $g(x) = -3x + 2$

   a. Find $f(x) + g(x)$ d. Find $f(a + 2) + g(a + 3)$

   b. Find $f(x) - g(x)$ e. For what value of x is $f(x) = -11$?

   c. Find $f(-3) + g(-4)$ f. For what value of x is $g(x) = -7$?

Lesson 23: Function Notation

Solutions

1. Let $f(x) = x + 4$ and $g(x) = 2x - 3$

   a. Find $f(x) + g(x)$

$$f(x) + g(x) = (x + 4) + (2x - 3)$$
$$= 3x + 1$$

Add the two functions together.

   b. Find $f(x) - g(x)$

$$f(x) - g(x) = (x + 4) - (2x - 3)$$
$$= -x + 7$$

Subtract $g(x)$ from $f(x)$.

   c. Find $f(2) + g(-2)$

$$f(2) + g(-2) = (2 + 4) + [2(-2) - 3]$$
$$= 6 - 4 - 3$$
$$= -1$$

Find the value of f when $x = 2$ and add it to the value of g when $x = -2$.

   d. Find $f(a) + g(a)$

$$f(a) + g(a) = (a + 4) + (2a - 3)$$
$$= 3a + 1$$

Replace x with a, then add the two.

   e. For what value of x is $f(x) = 5$?

$$5 = x + 4$$
$$1 = x$$

Find the value of x when the function $f(x)$ equals 5.

   f. For what value of x is $g(x) = 17$?

$$17 = 2x - 3$$
$$20 = 2x$$
$$10 = x$$

Find the value of x when the function $g(x)$ equals 17.

2. Let $f(x) = 2x - 5$ and $g(x) = -3x + 2$

   a. Find $f(x) + g(x)$

$$f(x) + g(x) = (2x - 5) + (-3x + 2)$$
$$= -x - 3$$

Add the two functions together.

   b. Find $f(x) - g(x)$

$$f(x) - g(x) = (2x - 5) - (-3x + 2)$$
$$= 2x - 5 + 3x - 2$$
$$= 5x - 7$$

Subtract $g(x)$ from $f(x)$.

   c. Find $f(-3) + g(-4)$

$$f(-3) + g(-4) = 2(-3) - 5 - 3(-4) + 2$$
$$= -6 - 5 + 12 + 2$$
$$= 3$$

Find the value of f when $x = -3$ and add it to the value of g when $x = -4$.

   d. Find $f(a + 2) + g(a + 3)$

$$f(a + 2) + g(a + 3) = 2(a + 2) - 5 - 3(a + 3) + 2$$
$$= 2a + 4 - 5 - 3a - 9 + 2$$
$$= -a - 8$$

Replace x with $a + 2$, then add the two functions.

   e. For what value of x is $f(x) = -11$?

$$-11 = 2x - 5$$
$$-6 = 2x$$
$$-3 = x$$

Find the value of x when the function $f(x)$ equals -11.

   f. For what value of x is $g(x) = -7$?

$$-7 = -3x + 2$$
$$-9 = -3x$$
$$3 = x$$

Find the value of x when the function $g(x)$ equals -7.

Linear functions can be used as models to predict things. They are often used in sports to try to predict when certain events will happen based on past history. Here is how it might work. Barry Bonds plays baseball for the San Francisco Giants. In 2001, he hit home runs at a record pace. After the first one-quarter of the season, people were saying that if he continued to hit home runs at his current pace he would break Mark McGuire's record for the most home runs in a single season of 70. They made that prediction by looking at a number of data points and developing an equation. The independent variable in the equation would represent the number of games played and the dependent variable would stand for the number of home runs hit.

The number of home runs is *a function of* the number of games played. Here is how an equation for that function might have been developed. Let's assume his home run production was reflected in the table below.

Games Played	Home Runs
0	0
10	6
20	10
30	14
40	18

Let's plot these points to see if they appear to be linearly related (that is, do the points fall generally in a straight line). When we do this we create what is called a *scattergram*.

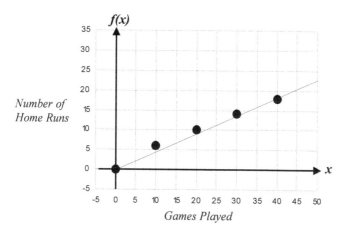

From the above graph, the points do appear to be *approximately linearly related*. With linear data we can develop an equation by knowing two data points. We can pick any two points to develop an equation of a line, but here we need to pick the two data points that <u>best</u> represent the line that we have drawn. For this graph, let's pick the point (0,0) which represents the start of the season, and (40,18) which represents about one-fourth of the season. Using these two points we develop the slope of the line:

$$m = \frac{y_2 - y_1}{x_2 - x_1} = \frac{18 - 0}{40 - 0} = \frac{9}{20}$$

Since the table contains the point (0,0), $b=0$ in the slope intercept form of a linear equation and our function is:

$$f(x) = \frac{9}{20}x, \qquad \text{where } x \text{ is the number of games played and } f(x) \text{ is the number of home runs hit.}$$

Lesson 24: The Basics of Modeling with Linear Functions

This function is called a model or a mathematical description of a set of data. Let's now use this model to see its prediction capabilities.

Example 1. Estimate the number of home runs Barry Bonds will hit in a full season of 162 games. In other words, find $f(162)$. To do this, we substitute 162 for x and we have:

$$f(162) = \frac{9}{20}(162) = 72.9$$

The model says that based on the data from the first part of the season, Barry Bonds would hit about 73 home runs. Since he did hit 73 in 2001, the model was very accurate.

Example 2. Girl Scout Troop ABCD sells Girl Scout Cookies each year. Their sales, starting in 1980 are shown in the table below. We will graph this data in a scattergram and then see if the data are approximately linearly related. Then, we will develop an equation that models the data. Finally, we will make some predictions using the model we develop.

Years	Boxes Sold
1980	250
1982	300
1984	475
1986	625
1988	650
1990	800
1992	825

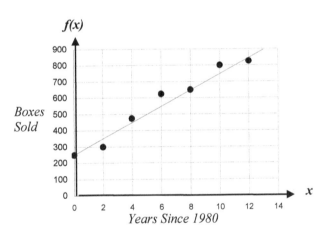

First note that the data are approximately linearly related. Now we need to find an equation of a line that best represents the data. If we selected the points (1982, 300) and (1984, 475), the resulting line would be too steep (slope too large). If we selected the points (1990, 800) and (1992, 810), the resulting line would be too shallow (slope too small). The line resulting from the points (1980, 250) and (1988, 650) seems to do a good job of representing the data so we will use those two points to develop our model. To simplify the calculations, we will let year 1980 be 0, 1982 be 2, 1984 be 4, and so on. Here is the calculation:

$$m = \frac{650 - 250}{8 - 0} = \frac{400}{8} = 50$$

We now find b by substituting the slope and one of the points into the slope intercept form of a linear equation as follows:

$$y = mx + b$$
$$250 = 50(0) + b$$
$$250 = b$$

132

So, the function that models the cookie sales of the Girl Scout Troop is:

$$f(x) = 50x + 250$$

Now let's use the model to predict the expected cookie sales in 1996, which is year 16 in our model.

$$f(16) = 50(16) + 250 = 1050$$

The Troop expects to sell 1,050 boxes of cookies in 1996.

Another use of the model is to determine the year in which cookie sales might reach a certain number. For example, when will cookie sales reach 1250 boxes? To determine this, we find what x will be when $f(x) = 1250$.

$$f(x) = 50x + 250$$
$$1250 = 50x + 250$$
$$1000 = 50x$$
$$20 = x$$

Add 20 to year 1980 and you get 2000. So, the model predicts it will be the year 2000 that cookie sales will reach 1250 boxes.

Example 3. The breakdown by sex of college graduates has shown a steady increase for females over the past two decades and is reflected in the table below.
a. Develop a scattergram and then develop an equation that models this data.
b. Determine the percent of females graduating in the year 2010.
c. Predict when the percent of the graduating class will be 75% female.
d. Predict when half the graduates will be female.

Years	% Female grads
1980	34
1985	42
1990	47
1995	52
2000	60

For part a, develop a scattergram:

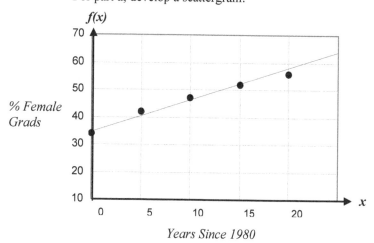

Years Since 1980

Now, develop an equation using the two data points that result in the line that best represents the data. In this case, the points chosen are (1980, 34) and (1995, 52). For ease of computations, let the year 1980 be 0 on the x-axis. So, we now measure time in years since 1980. This means the year 2000 is 20 on the x-axis.

133

Using our two points we first find the slope of the line:

$$m = \frac{52-34}{15-0} = \frac{18}{15} = 1.2$$

Now, let's continue to develop an equation that models this data.

$y = mx + b$
$34 = 1.2(0) + b$
$34 = b$

Substitute the point (0, 34) into the slope intercept form of a linear equation and solve for b.

Now we have enough information to generate the model: $f(x) = 1.2x + 34$

Now, we will use the model to answer our questions.

b. Determine the percent of females graduating in the year 2010.

Since we are using 1980 as our base year ($x = 0$), the year 2010 will be represented by $x = 30$.

$f(x) = 1.2x + 34$
$f(30) = 1.2(30) + 34$
$f(30) = 70$

This means that the model predicts that 70% of the 2010 graduating class will be female.

c. Predict when the percent of the graduating class will be 75% female.

For this we want to set the function value equal to 75 and solve for x.

$75 = 1.2x + 34$
$41 = 1.2x$
$34 \cong x$

Subtract 34 from each side and then divide each side by 1.2. We round the answer to the nearest whole number.

This means that about 34 years after 1980 (or 2014) the graduating class will be 75% female.

d. Predict when half the graduates will be female.

This part of the problem is asking us to find out when the female percentage was 50%. So, we set the function value equal to 50 and solve for x.

$50 = 1.2x + 34$
$16 = 1.2x$
$13 \cong x$

Subtract 34 from each side and then divide each side by 1.2. We round the answer to the nearest whole number.

This means that about 13 years after 1980 (or about 1993), the percent of the graduating class was about equal between male and female.

Lesson 24: The Basics of Modeling with Linear Functions

All models have limitations. For example, we could use this model to predict when the percent of graduates would be 100% female. By setting the function value to 100, we can solve for x:

$$100 = 1.2x + 34$$
$$66 = 1.2x$$
$$55 = x$$

We find that the model predicts that year to be 2035 (1980+55). Since it is highly unlikely that no males would be graduating from college in 2035, we would say that the *model breakdown* has occurred.

In a similar manner, we could use the model to predict when no females graduated from college. For this calculation we set the function value to 0 and solve for x as follows:

$$0 = 1.2x + 34$$
$$1.2x = -34$$
$$x \cong -28$$

Notice that the answer is a negative number. The negative sign indicates that we are talking about years *prior* to 1980. So we have to subtract 28 from 1980 and we see that the model predicted that it would have been 1952 that no females graduated from college. Again, we have model breakdown. So, models have good features, but we have to be careful how we use them.

Now it's your turn to try some modeling problems.

Lesson 24: The Basics of Modeling with Linear Functions

Lesson 24: The Basics of Modeling with Linear Functions

Exercises

1. A couple is saving for their retirement. Over the past 10 years, their savings has grown as shown in the table below. They feel they need $500,000 in their account in order to supplement their social security income.
   a) Develop a scattergram to see if the data are approximately linearly related.

Year	Money Saved (in thousands of dollars)
1990	$150
1992	$177
1994	$208
1996	$234
1998	$261
2000	$290

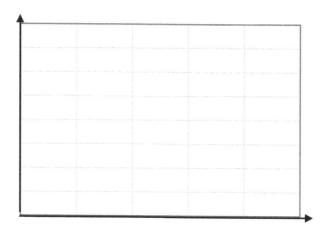

   b) Develop a model that represents their savings history.

   c) When will this couple reach their goal?

   d) How much will they have in 2010?

Lesson 24: The Basics of Modeling with Linear Functions

2. The price of homes has steadily increased over the past several decades. In Montgomery County, the cost of an average house has grown as shown in the table below.
    a) Develop a scattergram to see if the data are approximately linearly related.

Year	Average home value (in thousands)
1975	$75
1980	$105
1985	$150
1990	$200
1995	$230
2000	$275

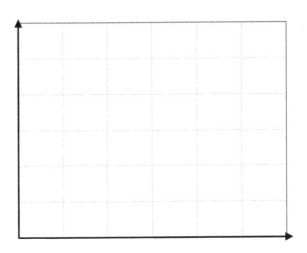

    b) Develop a model from this data.

    c) How much will an average home cost in 2025?

    d) When will the average cost be $600K?

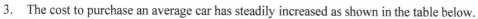

3. The cost to purchase an average car has steadily increased as shown in the table below.
   a) Develop a scattergram to see if the data are approximately linearly related.

Year	Average car cost (in thousands)
1980	$10.5
1985	$12.0
1990	$13.4
1995	$15.1
2000	$16.5

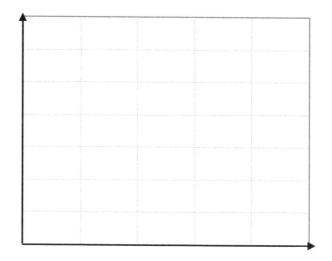

   b) Develop a model from this data.

   c) How much will it cost to buy a car in 2005? in 2010?

   d) When will an average car cost $25,000.

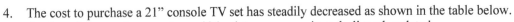

4. The cost to purchase a 21" console TV set has steadily decreased as shown in the table below.
    a) Develop a scattergram to see if the data are approximately linearly related.

Year	Cost of TV set
1982	$620
1985	$575
1988	$539
1991	$492
1994	$455
1997	$410
2000	$368

    b) Develop a model from this data.

    c) What will a TV set cost in 2008?

    d) When will the TV set sell for $150?

The data in these exercises are hypothetical.

Lesson 24: The Basics of Modeling with Linear Functions

Solutions

1. A couple is saving for their retirement. Over the past 10 years, their savings has grown as shown in the table below. They feel they need $500,000 in their account in order to supplement their social security income.
   a) Develop a scattergram to see if the data are approximately linearly related.
   b) Develop a model that represents their savings history
   c) When will this couple reach their goal?
   d) How much will they have in 2010?

Year	Money Saved (in thousands)
1990	$150
1992	$177
1994	$208
1996	$234
1998	$261
2000	$290

a) Scattergram:

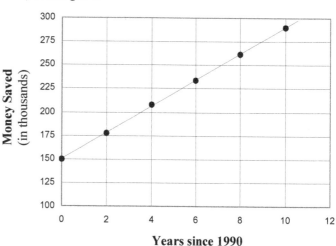

Years since 1990

The scattergram shows that the data are approximately linearly related. Therefore, we can select two points that best represent the line we have drawn through the data points. To develop this answer, we have chosen the first and last points. If you chose other points, your answer could differ slightly. To simplify the computations, we will let time be represented by the number of years since 1990. That means that the year 1990 is represented by 0 and the year 2000 is represented by 10.

Find the slope of the line: $m = \dfrac{290 - 150}{10 - 0} = \dfrac{140}{10} = 14$

Find the value of b: $y = mx + b$
$$150 = 14(0) + b$$
$$150 = b$$

b) Generate the model: $f(x) = 14x + 150$

c) When will $f(x) = 500$? $500 = 14x + 150$
$$350 = 14x$$
$$25 = x$$

Since we have used 1990 as 0, then this couple will reach their goal of $500,000 saved in 1990 + 25 or **year 2015.**

d) How much will they have saved by 2010? $f(x) = 14(20) + 150$
$$f(x) = 280 + 150$$
$$f(x) = 430$$

The year 2010 is represented by 20. Substituting 20 for x yields an answer of 430. This means they will have saved **$430,000** by 2010.

2. The price of homes has steadily increased over the past several decades. In Montgomery County, the cost of an average house has grown as shown in the table below.
    a) Develop a scattergram to see if the data are approximately linearly related.
    b) Develop a model from this data.
    c) How much will an average home cost in 2025?
    d) When will an average home cost $600K?

Year	Average home value (in thousands)
1975	$75
1980	$105
1985	$150
1990	$200
1995	$230
2000	$275

a) Scattergram:

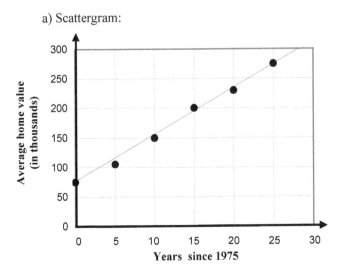

The scattergram shows that the data are approximately linearly related.   Therefore, we can select two points that best represent the line we have drawn through the data points. To develop this answer we have chosen the first and last points. If you chose other points, your answer could differ slightly. To simplify the computations, we will let time be represented by the number of years since 1975. That means that the year 1975 is represented by 0 and the year 2000 is represented by 25.

Find the slope of the line: $m = \dfrac{275-75}{25-0} = \dfrac{200}{25} = 8$

Find the value of b: $y = mx + b$
$$75 = 8(0) + b$$
$$75 = b$$

b) Generate the model: $f(x) = 8x + 75$

c) How much is a home worth in 2025? $f(50) = 8(50) + 75$
$$f(50) = 475$$

The year 2025 is represented by $x = 50$. The value of the function at 50 is 475, which is **$475,000**.

d) When will the average home cost 600K? $600 = 8x + 75$
$$525 = 8x$$
$$x \cong 66$$

An average home will cost $600K about the year 2041.

3. The cost to purchase an average car has steadily increased as shown in the table below.
    a) Develop a scattergram to see if the data are approximately linearly related.
    b) Develop a model from this data.
    c) How much will it cost to buy a car in 2005? in 2010?
    d) When will an average car cost $25,000?

Year	Average car cost (in thousands)
1980	$10.5
1986	$12.0
1990	$13.4
1995	$15.1
2000	$16.5

a) Scattergram:

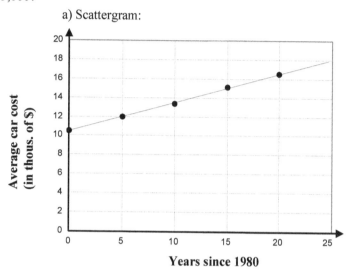

Years since 1980

The scattergram shows that the data are approximately linearly related. Therefore, we can select two points that best represent the line we have drawn through the data points. To develop this answer we have chosen the first and last points. If you chose other points, your answer could differ slightly. To simplify the computations, we will let time be represented by the number of years since 1980. That means that the year 1980 is represented by 0 and the year 2000 is represented by 20.

Find the slope of the line: $m = \dfrac{16.5 - 10.5}{20 - 0} = \dfrac{6}{20} = \dfrac{3}{10} = .3$

Find the value of b: $y = mx + b$
$$10.5 = .3(0) + b$$
$$10.5 = b$$

b) Generate the model: $f(x) = .3x + 10.5$

c) Cost to buy car in 2005: $f(25) = .3(25) + 10.5$
$$f(25) = 7.5 + 10.5$$
$$f(25) = 18$$

The cost to buy a car in 2005 is estimated by the model to be **$18,000**.

c) Cost to buy car in 2010 $f(30) = .3(30) + 10.5$
$$f(30) = 9 + 10.5$$
$$f(30) = 19.5$$

The cost to buy a car in 2010 is estimated by the model to be **$19,500**.

d) When will a car cost $25,000? $25 = .3x + 10.5$
$$14.5 = .3x$$
$$48 \cong x$$

A car will cost $25,000 about the **year 2028** (1980 + 48).

143

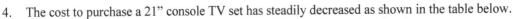
4. The cost to purchase a 21" console TV set has steadily decreased as shown in the table below.
a) Develop a scattergram to see if the data are approximately linearly related.
b) Develop a model from this data.
c) What will a TV set cost in 2008?
d) When will the TV set sell for $150?

Year	Cost of TV set
1982	$620
1985	$575
1988	$539
1991	$492
1994	$455
1997	$410
2000	$368

a) Scattergram:

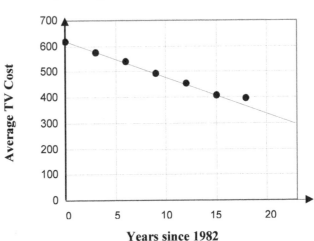

Years since 1982

The scattergram shows that the data are approximately linearly related. Therefore, we can select two points that best represent the line we have drawn through the data points. To develop this answer we have chosen the first point (1982, 620) and next to last point (1997, 410). If you chose other points, your answer could differ slightly. To simplify the computations, we will let time be represented by the number of years since 1982. That means that the year 1982 is represented by 0 and the year 1997 is represented by 15.

Find the slope of the line: $m = \dfrac{410-620}{15-0} = \dfrac{-210}{15} = -14$

Note that this slope is negative, which agrees with the scattergram.

Find the value of b: $y = mx + b$

$$620 = -14(0) + b$$
$$620 = b$$

b) Generate the model: $f(x) = -14x + 620$

c) Cost for TV in 2008: $f(26) = -14(26) + 620$ The TV will cost **$256** in the year 2008.

$$f(26) = -364 + 620$$
$$f(26) = 256$$

d) When will the set sell for $150? $150 = -14x + 620$

$$-470 = -14x$$
$$34 \cong x$$

The set will cost $150 approximately in the **year 2016** (1982 + 34).

Lesson 25: Rational Exponents

Let's start by discussing fractions as exponents – we call them rational exponents. Here are some examples:

Example 1. $25^{\frac{1}{2}}$ **Example 2.** $8^{\frac{1}{3}}$ **Example 3.** $16^{\frac{3}{4}}$

The meaning of the rational exponent ½ in **Example 1** is the same as a square root symbol. We want the number, when multiplied by itself, that will give us the base number - in this case 25. That number is 5. In **Example 2**, we are looking for the third root or the number which when multiplied by itself three times will yield the base number. In this case, the number is 2. **Example 3** needs additional explanation. The denominator of the rational exponent indicates that we want the fourth root of 16, which is 2. The numerator says we now want to raise 2 to the third power. The answer is 8. So, in summary we have:

$$25^{\frac{1}{2}} = \pm 5 \qquad\qquad 8^{\frac{1}{3}} = 2 \qquad\qquad 16^{\frac{3}{4}} = (16^{\frac{1}{4}})^3 = (\pm 2)^3 = \pm 8$$

Now let's try some additional examples:

Example 4. $27^{\frac{2}{3}} = (27^{\frac{1}{3}})^2 = 3^2 = 9$

Here we take the third root or cube root of 27 which is 3, and then we square 3, which yields 9.

Example 5. $(-8)^{\frac{1}{3}} = -2$

What number multiplied by itself three times will give a result of –8 ? Only –2 gives the desired result.

Example 6. $25^{\frac{3}{2}} = (25^{\frac{1}{2}})^3 = (\pm 5)^3 = \pm 125$

In this problem, we want the second root or square root of 25 which is 5 and we then want to cube 5 and we get 125.

Now let's combine our knowledge of fractions and our knowledge of the properties of exponents. Consider the following examples.

Example 7. $x^{\frac{3}{5}} x^{\frac{1}{5}} = x^{\frac{3}{5}+\frac{1}{5}} = x^{\frac{4}{5}}$

When two factors have the same base we use the product rule for exponents and we add the exponents. So, in this case we add two like fractions.

Example 8. $x^{\frac{1}{2}} x^{\frac{1}{3}} = x^{\frac{1}{2}+\frac{1}{3}} = x^{\frac{3}{6}+\frac{2}{6}} = x^{\frac{5}{6}}$

When the fractions don't have the same denominator, find the LCD, write equivalent fractions and then add.

Example 9. $\dfrac{x^{\frac{5}{8}}}{x^{\frac{3}{8}}} = x^{\frac{5}{8}-\frac{3}{8}} = x^{\frac{2}{8}} = x^{\frac{1}{4}}$

Remember when dividing, subtract exponents. Also, remember to reduce fractions to their lowest terms.

Example 10. $(5^{\frac{3}{5}})^5 = 5^{\frac{3\cdot5}{5}} = 5^{\frac{15}{5}} = 5^3 = 125$

The power rule for exponents says that you multiply the exponents.

Now try some exercises.

146

Lesson 25: Rational Exponents

Exercises

1. Simplify: $64^{\frac{2}{3}}$

2. Simplify: $16^{\frac{3}{2}}$

3. Simplify: $64^{\frac{5}{6}}$

4. Simplify: $1000^{\frac{2}{3}}$

5. Simplify: $5^{\frac{2}{5}} \bullet 5^{\frac{8}{5}}$

6. Simplify: $\dfrac{x^{\frac{3}{4}}}{x^{\frac{1}{3}}}$

7. Simplify: 5^{-3}

8. Simplify: $125^{\frac{2}{3}}$

9. Simplify: $x^{\frac{2}{3}} \bullet x^{\frac{1}{5}}$

10. Simplify: $(x^{\frac{3}{2}})^{\frac{1}{2}}$

11. Simplify: $2^{\frac{3}{4}} \bullet 2^{\frac{1}{4}}$

12. Simplify: $243^{\frac{3}{5}}$

13. Simplify: $81^{-\frac{1}{2}}$

14. Simplify: $\left(\dfrac{1}{3}\right)^{-2}$

Lesson 25: Rational Exponents

Solutions

1. Simplify: $64^{\frac{2}{3}} = (64^{\frac{1}{3}})^2 = 4^2 = 16$

8. Simplify: $125^{\frac{2}{3}} = (125^{\frac{1}{3}})^2 = 5^2 = 25$

2. Simplify: $16^{\frac{3}{2}} = (16^{\frac{1}{2}})^3 = (\pm 4)^3 = \pm 64$

9. Simplify: $x^{\frac{2}{3}} \bullet x^{\frac{1}{5}} = x^{\frac{2}{3}+\frac{1}{5}} = x^{\frac{10}{15}+\frac{3}{15}} = x^{\frac{13}{15}}$

3. Simplify: $64^{\frac{5}{6}} = (64^{\frac{1}{6}})^5 = (\pm 2)^5 = \pm 32$

10. Simplify: $(x^{\frac{3}{2}})^{\frac{1}{2}} = x^{\frac{3}{2} \bullet \frac{1}{2}} = x^{\frac{3}{4}}$

4. Simplify: $1000^{\frac{2}{3}} = (1000^{\frac{1}{3}})^2 = 10^2 = 100$

11. Simplify: $2^{\frac{3}{4}} \bullet 2^{\frac{1}{4}} = 2^{\frac{3}{4}+\frac{1}{4}} = 2^1 = 2$

5. Simplify: $5^{\frac{2}{5}} \bullet 5^{\frac{8}{5}} = 5^{\frac{2}{5}+\frac{8}{5}} = 5^{\frac{10}{5}} = 5^2 = 25$

12. Simplify: $243^{\frac{3}{5}} = (243^{\frac{1}{5}})^3 = 3^3 = 27$

6. Simplify: $\dfrac{x^{\frac{3}{4}}}{x^{\frac{1}{3}}} = x^{\frac{3}{4}-\frac{1}{3}} = x^{\frac{9}{12}-\frac{4}{12}} = x^{\frac{5}{12}}$

13. Simplify: $81^{-\frac{1}{2}} = \dfrac{1}{81^{\frac{1}{2}}} = \pm\dfrac{1}{9}$

7. Simplify: $5^{-3} = \dfrac{1}{5^3} = \dfrac{1}{125}$

14. Simplify: $\left(\dfrac{1}{3}\right)^{-2} = 3^2 = 9$

Lesson 26: Exponential Functions

Let's now turn our attention to exponential functions. When we say *exponential function*, we are talking about a function that has the variable as the exponent. Examples are:

$$f(x) = 2^x \qquad\qquad g(x) = 2(5)^x \qquad\qquad h(x) = -3\left(\frac{1}{2}\right)^x$$

In each case, the variable x is the exponent. In general terms, we can say that an exponential function is one that can be put in the form of:

$$f(x) = ab^x$$

But we have to put some restrictions on a and b. The term a cannot be zero (otherwise the function would equal zero) and the term b has to be positive (greater than zero) and it cannot equal 1. If it equaled 1, then the exponent would have no effect since 1 raised to any power is still 1 and the function would be the linear function $f(x) = a$.

Let's see what an exponential function looks like when we graph it on the rectangular coordinate system.

Example 1. Sketch the exponential function: $f(x) = 2^x$

Set up a table of values that satisfy the function, then graph the function.

x	$f(x)$
-2	$2^{-2} = \dfrac{1}{2^2} = \dfrac{1}{4}$
-1	$2^{-1} = \dfrac{1}{2}$
0	$2^0 = 1$
1	$2^1 = 2$
2	$2^2 = 4$
3	$2^3 = 8$

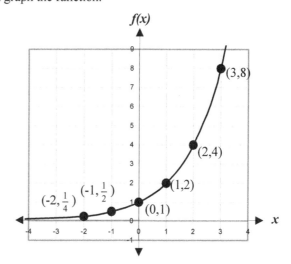

Note that the curve increases quite rapidly as x increases. As x decreases, the y value becomes smaller and smaller but never equals 0.

149

Lesson 26: Exponential Functions

In **example 1**, we had the general form of an exponential function with $a = 1$ and $b = 2$. Let's look at what happens to the curve when we change the values a and b and change the sign of a. First consider increasing the value of b from 2 to 3 or 4 or more. Below is a table of points for the functions noted.

x	$f(x) = 3^x$	$g(x) = 4^x$	$h(x) = 10^x$
-2	$\dfrac{1}{9}$	$\dfrac{1}{16}$	$\dfrac{1}{100}$
-1	$\dfrac{1}{3}$	$\dfrac{1}{4}$	$\dfrac{1}{10}$
0	1	1	1
1	3	4	10
2	9	16	100
3	27	64	1000

Note that all the functions have one point in common $(0,1)$, which is the y intercept. Also, for all these functions, as the x value increases, the function value increases rapidly. We say the function increases exponentially.

Now, let b have a value between 0 and 1 and note the effect on the graph.

Example 2. Sketch the exponential function: $f(x) = \left(\dfrac{1}{2}\right)^x$

We, again, begin by generating a table of values, then we graph the function:

x	$f(x)$
-3	$\left(\dfrac{1}{2}\right)^{-3} = 2^3 = 8$
-2	$\left(\dfrac{1}{2}\right)^{-2} = 2^2 = 4$
-1	$\left(\dfrac{1}{2}\right)^{-1} = 2^1 = 2$
0	$\left(\dfrac{1}{2}\right)^{0} = 1$
1	$\left(\dfrac{1}{2}\right)^{1} = \dfrac{1}{2}$
2	$\left(\dfrac{1}{2}\right)^{2} = \dfrac{1}{4}$

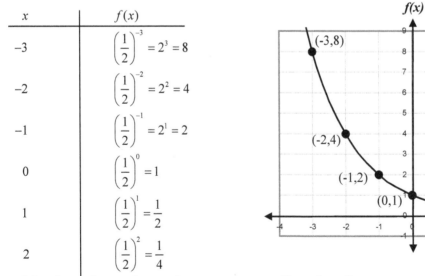

This graph is a decreasing graph – as x increases, y gets smaller and smaller.

Consider how the graph changes as the base approaches 1. If $b = 1$, the function is the horizontal line $f(x) = a$. So, as the value of the fraction in the base approaches 1, the curve flattens out until it becomes a horizontal line. Now let's look at some examples with various a values.

Example 3. Sketch the exponential function: $f(x) = -2(2)^x$

x	$f(x)$
-2	$-2(2)^{-2} = -2\left(\dfrac{1}{2^2}\right) = -2\left(\dfrac{1}{4}\right) = -\dfrac{1}{2}$
-1	$-2(2)^{-1} = -2\left(\dfrac{1}{2^1}\right) = -1$
0	$-2(2)^0 = -2$
1	$-2(2)^1 = -4$
2	$-2(2)^2 = -8$
3	$-2(2)^3 = -16$

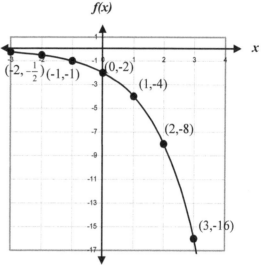

In this example, as x increases, the y value becomes smaller and smaller. Notice also that the y values are always negative. That is the effect of $a < 0$. Now let's look at one more example. This one will have $a < 0$ and b between 0 and 1.

Example 4. Sketch the exponential function: $f(x) = -3\left(\dfrac{1}{4}\right)^x$

x	$f(x)$
-3	$-3\left(\dfrac{1}{4}\right)^{-3} = -3(4^3) = -192$
-2	$-3\left(\dfrac{1}{4}\right)^{-2} = -3(4^2) = -48$
-1	$-3\left(\dfrac{1}{4}\right)^{-1} = -3(4^1) = -12$
0	$-3\left(\dfrac{1}{4}\right)^0 = -3$
1	$-3\left(\dfrac{1}{4}\right)^1 = -\dfrac{3}{4}$
2	$-3\left(\dfrac{1}{4}\right)^2 = -3(4)^2 = -\dfrac{3}{16}$

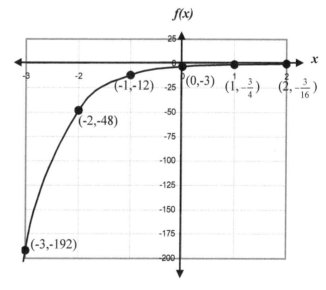

In this case, the function is increasing since the y value gets larger as x increases. But in this case also, y is always negative because a is a negative number.

Now try some exponential function problems.

151

Lesson 26: Exponential Functions

Lesson 26: Exponential Functions

Exercises

1. Set up a table of values and sketch the four exponential functions on the graphs below:

$$f(x) = 5^x \qquad g(x) = \left(\frac{1}{4}\right)^x \qquad h(x) = -2(3)^x \qquad j(x) = -2\left(\frac{1}{2}\right)^x$$

x	$f(x)$	$g(x)$	$h(x)$	$j(x)$
−3				
−2				
−1				
0				
1				
2				
3				

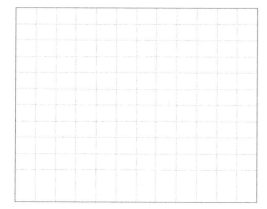
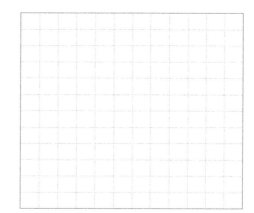
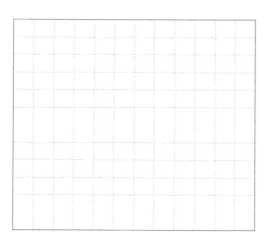
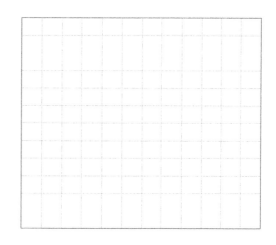

153

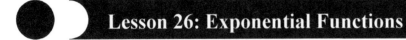
Solutions

1. Set up a table of values and sketch the four exponential functions on the graphs below:

$$f(x) = 5^x \qquad g(x) = \left(\frac{1}{4}\right)^x \qquad h(x) = -2(3)^x \qquad j(x) = -2\left(\frac{1}{2}\right)^x$$

x	$f(x)$
-3	$\frac{1}{125}$
-2	$\frac{1}{25}$
-1	$\frac{1}{5}$
0	1
1	5
2	25
3	125

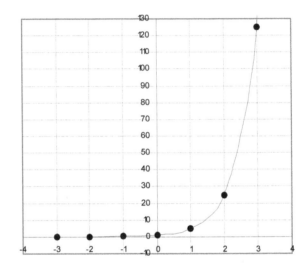

x	$g(x)$
-3	64
-2	16
-1	4
0	1
1	$\frac{1}{4}$
2	$\frac{1}{16}$
3	$\frac{1}{64}$

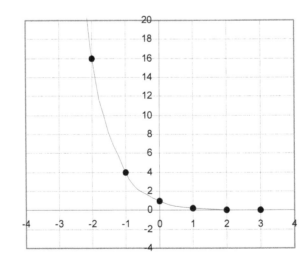

x	h(x)
-3	$-\dfrac{2}{27}$
-2	$-\dfrac{2}{9}$
-1	$-\dfrac{2}{3}$
0	-2
1	-6
2	-18
3	-54

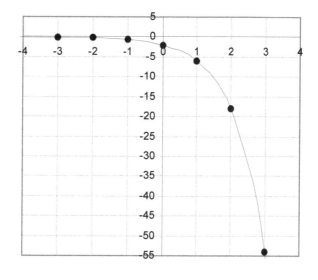

x	j(x)
-3	-16
-2	-8
-1	-4
0	-2
1	-1
2	$-\dfrac{1}{2}$
3	$-\dfrac{1}{4}$

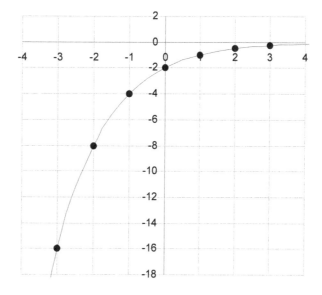

Lesson 26: Exponential Functions

Lesson 27: More on Exponential Functions

In Lesson 24, we learned how to find a linear equation from a table of values. If that table of values contained the point with $x = 0$, the generation of the linear equation was quite simple. Consider this table of values:

x	$f(x)$
0	4
1	7
2	10
3	13

From the table, we know the y intercept $(0,4)$, so we know the value of b (4) in the slope intercept form of a linear equation. We can find the slope m by substituting an ordered pair into the slope intercept form as follows:

$$y = mx + b$$
$$7 = m(1) + 4$$
$$3 = m$$

Substitute the point $(1,7)$ into the slope intercept form of a linear equation and solve for the slope, m.

We could also find the slope from the table by noticing how y changes when x changes by 1. In the table, $f(x)$ or y changes by 3 each time x increases by 1. This is the slope. For any linear equation, the slope is amount of change in y as x increases by 1. So, the equation of the line represented by the above table of values is: $y = 3x + 4$

We can use a similar process to derive an exponential equation from a table of values. To do that we need to understand the base multiplier property.

The Base Multiplier Property

For an exponential function in the standard form $y = ab^x$, as the value of the independent variable x, increases by 1, the value of the dependent variable y is **multiplied** by the base b.

A Rule to Remember!

Let's look at the table of values we used in the lesson 26 exercises and see if we can derive the exponential equations.

x	$f(x)$	$g(x)$	$h(x)$	$j(x)$
-3	$\dfrac{1}{125}$	64	$\dfrac{-2}{27}$	-16
-2	$\dfrac{1}{25}$	16	$\dfrac{-2}{9}$	-8
-1	$\dfrac{1}{5}$	4	$\dfrac{-2}{3}$	-4
0	1	1	-2	-2
1	5	$\dfrac{1}{4}$	-6	-1
2	25	$\dfrac{1}{16}$	-18	$\dfrac{-1}{2}$
3	125	$\dfrac{1}{64}$	-54	$\dfrac{-1}{4}$

157

Look at the values of $f(x)$ as x increases by 1. Each time, the value of $f(x)$ is multiplied by 5. This means that the b value in the standard form of an exponential function is 5. The a value is determined by the value of the dependent variable, $f(x)$, when the independent variable is 0. This is the y intercept. In the case of $f(x)$ above, that value is 1. So, the equation for $f(x)$ is:

$$f(x) = 1(5)^x \qquad \text{or simply} \qquad f(x) = 5^x$$

For $g(x)$, using the base multiplier property, we find that the multiplier (or b value) is ¼ and that the a value or y intercept is 1. So, the equation for $g(x)$ is:

$$g(x) = \left(\frac{1}{4}\right)^x$$

For $h(x)$, the b value is 3 and the a value is –2, so the equation is:

$$h(x) = -2(3)^x$$

For $j(x)$, the b value is ½ and the a value is –2, so the equation is:

$$j(x) = -2\left(\frac{1}{2}\right)^x$$

Now, it's your turn.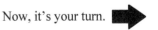

Lesson 27: More on Exponential Functions

Exercises

1. Determine if the following functions are linear or exponential and find an equation for each of them.

x	$f(x)$	$g(x)$	$h(x)$	$j(x)$
-2	1600	-2	$-\dfrac{1}{8}$	-5
-1	400	1	$-\dfrac{1}{2}$	-10
0	100	4	-2	-20
1	25	7	-8	-40
2	6.25	10	-32	-80

$f(x) =$

$g(x) =$

$h(x) =$

$j(x) =$

Lesson 27: More on Exponential Functions

Solutions

1. Determine if the following functions are linear or exponential and find an equation for each of them.

x	$f(x)$	$g(x)$	$h(x)$	$j(x)$
-2	1600	-2	$-\dfrac{1}{8}$	-5
-1	400	1	$-\dfrac{1}{2}$	-10
0	100	4	-2	-20
1	25	7	-8	-40
2	6.25	10	-32	-80

$f(x)$ is **exponential** since the function value changes by a multiple rather than a constant as x increases by 1. The multiple is ¼. Notice also that the function value is 100 when $x = 0$ (y-intercept), so in our standard form of an exponential function, a is 100 and b is ¼. We can write our equation as:

$$f(x) = a(b)^x$$
$$f(x) = 100\left(\frac{1}{4}\right)^x$$

$g(x)$ is **linear** since the function value changes by a constant as x increases by 1. That constant is 3, so that represents our slope. The y-intercept is at the point (0, 4), so the value of b in the slope intercept form of a linear equation is 4 and our equation for $g(x)$ is:

$$g(x) = mx + b$$
$$g(x) = 3x + 4$$

$h(x)$ is **exponential** since the function value increases by the multiple 4. The y-intercept is at (0, -2) so the exponential equation is:

$$h(x) = a(b)^x$$
$$h(x) = -2(4)^x$$

$j(x)$ is **exponential** since the function value increases by the multiple 2. The y-intercept is at (0, -20) so the exponential equation is:

$$j(x) = a(b)^x$$
$$j(x) = -20(2)^x$$

160

Lesson 28: Solving Equations with Constant Exponents

Now let's use our knowledge of exponents to solve some equations with constant exponents.

Remember how we solved linear equations? We used the addition property of equality to isolate the variable on one side of the equation and get the constants on the other side. Then we used the multiplication property of equality to get the variable to have a coefficient of 1. In the case of the following equations, we will use the same properties before we work on the exponent.

Example 1. $x^2 = 81$

We already have the variable term isolated and with a coefficient of 1. So here, we are looking for a number (or numbers) that when multiplied by itself will yield 81 (i.e. the square root of 81). There are two answers: ± 9.

Example 2. $5x^2 = 80$

The variable term is isolated on the left side but has a coefficient of 5. So, we divide each side by 5 and then work on the exponent.

$$\frac{5x^2}{5} = \frac{80}{5}$$
$$x^2 = 16$$
$$x = \pm 4$$

Example 3. $6a^3 - 5 = -53$

Use the addition property to isolate the variable term (by adding 5 to each side) and then use the multiplication property to have a coefficient of 1 (divide by 6). Then, find a number that when multiplied by itself three times will equal the desired number (i.e. the cube root).

$6a^3 = -48$ In this case, we only have one solution that works.
$a^3 = -8$ Negative 2 is the only number multiplied by itself
$a = -2$ three times will yield a negative 8.

Example 4. $5b^6 = 90$

Divide each side by 5 to develop a coefficient of 1 for the variable term and then resolve the exponent.

$b^6 = 18$

$b = \pm(18)^{\frac{1}{6}}$ Take the 6th root of both sides.

Unless we use a calculator, this is an acceptable answer. We are looking for a number that when multiplied by itself 6 times would equal 18. Such a number is not an integer.

Now, it's your turn. ➡

161

Lesson 28: Solving Equations with Constant Exponents

Lesson 28: Solving Equations with Constant Exponents

Exercises

1. Solve: $7x^2 = 63$

2. Solve: $6a^3 = 162$

3. Solve: $4x^2 + 5 = 69$

4. Solve: $5y^2 - 8 = 172$

5. Solve: $\dfrac{1}{6}x^2 + \dfrac{5}{3} = \dfrac{7}{2}$

6. Solve: $\dfrac{1}{2}x^2 + \dfrac{5}{4} = 3$

7. Solve: $3x^5 = 30$

8. Solve: $21x^2 = 63$

9. Solve: $5a^3 + 7 = 22$

10. Solve: $3x^4 - 8 = 40$

11. Solve: $5x^2 + 2 = 37$

12. Solve: $\dfrac{x^2}{5} + \dfrac{1}{3} = \dfrac{3}{5}$

13. Solve: $\dfrac{y^2}{14} - \dfrac{2}{7} = \dfrac{1}{2}$

14. Solve: $4x^3 = 11$

Solutions

1. Solve: $7x^2 = 63$

$$x^2 = 9$$

Answer: $x = \pm 3$

Divide each side by 7, then take the square root of each side.

2. Solve: $6a^3 = 162$

$$a^3 = 27$$

Answer: $a = 3$

Divide each side by 6, then take the cube root of each side. The answer is +3, but not –3.

3. Solve: $4x^2 + 5 = 69$

$$4x^2 = 64$$

$$x^2 = 16$$

Answer: $x = \pm 4$

Subtract 5 from each side, divide each side by 4, then take the square root of each side.

4. Solve: $5y^2 - 8 = 172$

$$5y^2 = 180$$

$$y^2 = 36$$

Answer: $y = \pm 6$

Add 8 to each side, divide by 5, then take the square of each side.

5. Solve $\dfrac{1}{6}x^2 + \dfrac{5}{3} = \dfrac{7}{2}$

$$x^2 + 10 = 21$$

$$x^2 = 11$$

Answer: $x = \pm\sqrt{11}$

For an equation with fractions, multiply by the LCD (in this case, 6), then solve by subtracting 10 from each side and taking the square root of each side.

6. Solve: $\dfrac{1}{2}x^2 + \dfrac{5}{4} = 3$

$$2x^2 + 5 = 12$$

$$2x^2 = 7$$

Answer: $x = \pm\sqrt{\dfrac{7}{2}}$

Multiply ALL terms by the LCD (in this case, 4) then solve.

7. Solve: $3x^5 = 30$

$$x^5 = 10$$

Answer: $x = 10^{\frac{1}{5}}$

Divide each side by 3, then take the 5th root of each side.

8. Solve: $21x^2 = 63$

$$x^2 = 3$$

Answer: $x = \pm\sqrt{3}$

Divide each side by 21, then take the square root of each side.

9. Solve: $5a^3 + 7 = 22$

$$5a^3 = 15$$
$$a^3 = 3$$

Answer: $a = 3^{\frac{1}{3}}$

Subtract 7 from each side, the divide each side by 5. Finally, take the cube root of each side.

10. Solve: $3x^4 - 8 = 40$

$$3x^4 = 48$$
$$x^4 = 16$$

Answer: $x = \pm 2$

Add 8 to each side, divide by 3, then take the 4th root of each side. Notice that since the exponent is even, the answer can be positive or negative.

11. Solve: $5x^2 + 2 = 37$

$$5x^2 = 35$$
$$x^2 = 7$$

Answer: $x = \pm\sqrt{7}$

Subtract 2 from each side, divide by 5, then take the square root of each side.

12. Solve: $\dfrac{x^2}{5} + \dfrac{1}{3} = \dfrac{3}{5}$

$$3x^2 + 5 = 9$$
$$3x^2 = 4$$

Answer: $x = \pm\sqrt{\dfrac{4}{3}}$

For an equation with fractions, multiply by the LCD (in this case, 15). Now, subtract 5 from each side and then divide by the coefficient of the variable, in this case, 3. Finally, take the square root of each side.

13. Solve: $\dfrac{y^2}{14} - \dfrac{2}{7} = \dfrac{1}{2}$

$$y^2 - 4 = 7$$
$$y^2 = 11$$

Answer: $y = \pm\sqrt{11}$

Multiply each side by the LCD, 14, then add 4 to each side, then take the square root of each side.

14. Solve: $4x^3 = 11$

$$x^3 = \dfrac{11}{4}$$

Answer: $x = \left(\dfrac{11}{4}\right)^{\frac{1}{3}}$

Multiply by the LCD, 14, then divide each side by 4, then take the cube root (3rd root) of each side.

Lesson 28: Solving Equations with Constant Exponents

Lesson 29: The Basics of Logarithmic Functions

Inverse Functions

To understand logarithmic functions, let's first learn about inverse functions. Given an ordered pair (3,2), the inverse is found by simply reversing the x and y values. So, the inverse of (3,2) is (2,3). We use a notation to designate an inverse of a function, which is: $f^{-1}(x)$. In this case the -1 is not an exponent, it is simply a method of denoting an inverse. Let's look at a table of values of a function and values of the inverse of the function.

Example 1. Find the inverse of the following ordered pairs:

x	$f(x)$		x	$f^{-1}(x)$
1	5		5	1
2	7		7	2
3	9		9	3
4	11		11	4

Notice that the input value for the function is the output value for the inverse. Since we are reversing the values of x and y, we can take a function and generate an inverse function by doing a few simple steps. The rule for the function $f(x)$ above is $f(x) = 2x + 3$. We can generate the inverse using the procedure in the following example.

Example 2. Find the inverse of $f(x) = 2x + 3$:

Step 1 – Substitute y for $f(x)$: $\qquad y = 2x + 3$

Step 2 – Solve for x: $\qquad x = \dfrac{1}{2}y - \dfrac{3}{2}$

Step 3 – Reverse x and y: $\qquad y = \dfrac{1}{2}x - \dfrac{3}{2}$

Step 4 – Substitute $f^{-1}(x)$ for y: $\qquad f^{-1}(x) = \dfrac{1}{2}x - \dfrac{3}{2}$

We can verify that we have the correct inverse by checking any of the ordered pairs of the inverse function in **Example 1**. Using the input value of 5, let's see if the inverse function value is 1.

$$f^{-1}(x) = \frac{1}{2}x - \frac{3}{2}$$

$$f^{-1}(5) = \frac{1}{2}(5) - \frac{3}{2}$$

$$f^{-1}(5) = \frac{5}{2} - \frac{3}{2} = 1$$

Basically, the inverse of a function turns inputs into outputs. Now let's look at the inverse of an exponential function.

Here is a table of values that represent the exponential function $f(x) = 2^x$:

x	$f(x)$
0	1
1	2
2	4
3	8

Below is a table for the exponential function (repeated from above) as well as the inverse of the exponential function:

x	$f(x)$	x	$f^{-1}(x)$
0	1	1	0
1	2	2	1
2	4	4	2
3	8	8	3

In words, the function is the base number 2 raised to the x power. The inverse function is the power to which we raise 2 to get x. Rather than call it the inverse of an exponential function we have a new name – a *logarithm*. So, an exponential function and a logarithmic function are inverses of each other. Here are a few examples of how it looks:

Exponential Function

$f(x) = 2^x$

$g(x) = 3^x$

$h(x) = 6^x$

Inverse Function

$f^{-1}(x) = \log_2 x$

$g^{-1}(x) = \log_3 x$

$h^{-1}(x) = \log_6 x$

The inverse function is read as "log, base b, of x".

> *When working with logarithms, it is important to remember that a logarithm is an exponent and that the base must be positive.*

Now, let's take a look at the relationship between exponential equations and logarithmic equations. Here is that relationship and it should be memorized:

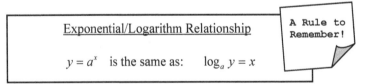

Exponential/Logarithm Relationship

A Rule to Remember!

$y = a^x$ is the same as: $\log_a y = x$

Maybe these examples will make it easier to understand.

Example 3. Write the following exponential equations as logarithmic equations:

Exponential Format | Logarithmic Format

a. $5^2 = 25$ $\log_5 25 = 2$

b. $4^3 = 64$ $\log_4 64 = 3$

c. $3^0 = 1$ $\log_3 1 = 0$

Example 4. Write the following logarithmic equations as exponential equations:

Logarithmic Format	Exponential Format
a. $\log_5 125 = 3$	$5^3 = 125$
b. $\log_2 32 = 5$	$2^5 = 32$
c. $\log_{10} 100 = 2$	$10^2 = 100$

Usually when working with logarithms, we need to specify the base. However, if the base is 10, we do not normally write the base. A logarithm with base 10 is called a common logarithm. So in **Example 4c** we could have written:

$$\log 100 = 2$$

Now it's your turn.

Lesson 29: The Basics of Logarithmic Functions

Lesson 29: The Basics of Logarithmic Functions

Exercises

Find the inverse of the following:

1. $f(x) = 3x - 7$

3. $h(x) = 4^x$

2. $g(x) = -4x + 5$

4. $j(x) = \log_7 x$

Write the following as logarithmic equations:

5. $5^3 = 125$

7. $7^0 = 1$

6. $4^2 = 16$

8. $b^a = c$

Write the following as exponential equations:

9. $\log_4 64 = 3$

11. $\log 1000 = 3$

10. $\log_3 81 = 4$

12. $\log_b x = y$

Lesson 29: The Basics of Logarithmic Functions

Solutions

Find the inverse of the following:

1. $f(x) = 3x - 7$

$y = 3x - 7$

$y + 7 = 3x$

$\frac{1}{3}y + \frac{7}{3} = x$

$y = \frac{1}{3}x + \frac{7}{3}$

Replace $f(x)$ with y. Solve for x (add 7 to each side, then divide each side by 3). Interchange x and y. Replace y with the inverse notation.

Answer: $f^{-1}(x) = \frac{1}{3}x + \frac{7}{3}$

3. $h(x) = 4^x$

Answer: $h^{-1}(x) = \log_4 x$

2. $g(x) = -4x + 5$

$y = -4x + 5$

$y - 5 = -4x$

$-\frac{1}{4}y + \frac{5}{4} = x$

$y = -\frac{1}{4}x + \frac{5}{4}$

Replace $g(x)$ with y. Solve for x (subtract 5 from each side, then divide each side by -4). Interchange x and y. Replace y with the inverse notation.

Answer: $g^{-1}(x) = -\frac{1}{4}x + \frac{5}{4}$

4. $j(x) = \log_7 x$

Answer: $j^{-1}(x) = 7^x$

Write the following as logarithmic equations:

5. $5^3 = 125$

Answer: $\log_5 125 = 3$

6. $4^2 = 16$

Answer: $\log_4 16 = 2$

7. $7^0 = 1$

Answer: $\log_7 1 = 0$

8. $b^a = c$

Answer: $\log_b c = a$

Write the following as exponential equations:

9. $\log_4 64 = 3$

Answer: $4^3 = 64$

10. $\log_3 81 = 4$

Answer: $3^4 = 81$

11. $\log 1000 = 3$

Answer: $10^3 = 1000$

12. $\log_b x = y$

Answer: $b^y = x$

Lesson 30: Solving Logarithmic Equations

We can use the knowledge of how to convert from exponential equations to logarithmic equations, and vice versa, to help us solve some equations. Consider the following examples:

Example 1. Solve for x: $\log_3 x = 4$

$$3^4 = x$$
$$81 = x$$

Convert to exponential format to solve this equation.

Example 2. Solve for x: $\log_2 x = -4$

$$2^{-4} = x$$
$$\frac{1}{2^4} = x$$
$$\frac{1}{16} = x$$

When we convert this to exponential format, we have to remember how to handle negative exponents.

Example 3. Solve for x: $\log 1000 = x$

$$10^x = 1000$$
$$x = 3$$

Since there is no base shown, it is a common log with base 10. Again, to solve we will convert to exponential format.

Example 4. Solve for b: $\log_b 16 = 2$

$$b^2 = 16$$
$$b = 4$$

In this case, we have to find the base, b. We do so by converting the equation to exponential format just as we did in the last few examples and then solving by taking the square root of both sides. Our answer is actually 4 and –4, but we must discard –4 because, according to our definition, the base must be positive.

Example 5. Solve for b: $\log_b 32 = 5$

$$b^5 = 32$$
$$b = 32^{\frac{1}{5}}$$
$$b = 2$$

Convert this example to exponential format and then take the 5th root of each side.

Now it's your turn.

Lesson 30: Solving Logarithmic Equations

Lesson 30: Solving Logarithmic Equations

Exercises

Solve the following for x:

1. $\log_4 x = 3$

2. $\log_3 x = 5$

3. $\log x = 0$

4. $\log_5 x = 4$

5. $\log_2 x = -3$

6. $\log_3 x = -2$

Solve the following for b:

7. $\log_b 49 = 2$

8. $\log_b 125 = 3$

Lesson 30: Solving Logarithmic Equations

Solutions

Solve the following for x:

1. $\log_4 x = 3$

$\quad 4^3 = x$

$\quad 64 = x$

Write in exponential format, then solve for x.

2. $\log_3 x = 5$

$\quad 3^5 = x$

$\quad 243 = x$

Write in exponential format, then solve for x.

3. $\log x = 0$

$\quad 10^0 = x$

$\quad 1 = x$

Since there is no base shown, it is a common log with base 10. Write in exponential format, then solve for x.

4. $\log_5 x = 4$

$\quad 5^4 = x$

$\quad 625 = x$

Write in exponential format, then solve for x.

5. $\log_2 x = -3$

$\quad 2^{-3} = x$

$\quad \dfrac{1}{2^3} = x$

$\quad \dfrac{1}{8} = x$

The process for solving this is the same as that used in the last three problems. However, this example involves a negative exponent.

6. $\log_3 x = -2$

$\quad 3^{-2} = x$

$\quad \dfrac{1}{3^2} = x$

$\quad \dfrac{1}{9} = x$

Another negative exponent.

Solve the following for b:

7. $\log_b 49 = 2$

$\quad b^2 = 49$

$\quad b = 7$

Here we have to solve for the base. We still start by writing in exponential format, but in this case we have to take the square root of each side to solve for b. Remember, the base must be positive.

8. $\log_b 125 = 3$

$\quad b^3 = 125$

$\quad b = 5$

Here we have to solve for the base. We still start by writing in exponential format, but in this case we have to take the cube root of each side to solve for b.

Lesson 31: Properties of Logarithms

The relationship between exponential functions and logarithms enables us to generate some useful rules for logarithms. Do you remember anything raised to a power of 0 is 1? So, $a^0 = 1$.

Well, that enables us to say $\log_a 1 = 0$. In words this is: "the log, to any base, of 1 is 0."

Here are some examples:

Example 1. $\log_5 1 = 0$

Example 2. $\log_3 1 = 0$

Here's another exponential relationship that is useful with logarithms: Any number raised to a power of 1 is that number itself or, in symbols $a^1 = a$.

This translates to the logarithmic equation $\log_a a = 1$. In words this is: "the log, base a, of a is 1."

Here are some examples of this relationship:

Example 3. $\log_8 8 = 1$

Example 4. $\log 10 = 1$

Another very useful property of logarithms that is derived from properties of exponents is the power property. The power property sounds complex and even looks complex but in practice it's pretty simple. The power property states that if you have a log of a number to a power, you can rewrite that as the power (exponent) times the log of the number. Here is what it looks like:

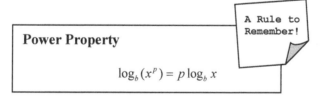

Power Property

$$\log_b (x^p) = p \log_b x$$

A Rule to Remember!

Here are some examples of how it works:

Example 5. $\log_4 (x^3) = 3 \log_4 x$

Example 6. $\log_3 (4^{2x+1}) = (2x+1) \log_3 4$

Now let's solve some equations using our knowledge of logarithms and exponents.

Example 7.   Solve: $3^x = 18$

We learned when solving linear equations that whatever we do to one side of an equation, we have do to the same thing to the other side. This holds true for taking the log of each side. When we do, we get:

$$\log(3^x) = \log 18 \qquad \text{Take the log of both sides.}$$
$$x \log 3 = \log 18 \qquad \text{Use the power property.}$$
$$x = \frac{\log 18}{\log 3} \qquad \text{Divide each side by log 3.}$$

We will leave the result like this. If you were using a calculator you could get a decimal answer.

Example 8.   Solve: $4(6^x) = 28$

Before we take the log of each side, we need to isolate the exponential expression on the left side by dividing by 4. Then, take the log of both sides, apply the power property, and finally divide by the coefficient of the variable.

$$\frac{4(6^x)}{4} = \frac{28}{4} \qquad \text{Divide each side by 4.}$$
$$6^x = 7$$
$$\log 6^x = \log 7 \qquad \text{Take the log of both sides.}$$
$$x \log 6 = \log 7 \qquad \text{Use the power property.}$$
$$x = \frac{\log 7}{\log 6} \qquad \text{Divide each side by log 6.}$$

Example 9.   Solve: $4^{2x+3} = 15$

Even though this looks more difficult, we follow the same steps as in the previous examples:

$$\log 4^{2x+3} = \log 15 \qquad \text{Take the log of both sides.}$$
$$(2x+3)\log 4 = \log 15 \qquad \text{Use the power property.}$$
$$2x+3 = \frac{\log 15}{\log 4} \qquad \text{Divide each side by log 4.}$$
$$2x = \frac{\log 15}{\log 4} - 3 \qquad \text{Subtract 3 from each side.}$$
$$x = \frac{\frac{\log 15}{\log 4} - 3}{2} \qquad \text{Divide each side by 2.}$$

Now it's your turn.

Lesson 31: Properties of Logarithms

Exercises

1. Solve: $\qquad$ $4^x = 12$

2. Solve: $\qquad$ $3^x = 16$

3. Solve: $\qquad$ $2(4^x) = 28$

4. Solve: $\qquad$ $5(2^x) = 25$

5. Solve: $\qquad$ $3^x + 5 = 17$

6. Solve: $\qquad$ $4 + 3(2^x) = 19$

7. Solve: $\qquad$ $5^{3x-1} = 12$

8. Solve: $\qquad$ $6^{4x+5} = 16$

9. Solve: $\qquad$ $4^{2x+6} = 20$

10. Solve: $\qquad$ $3^{3x-2} = 3$

Lesson 31: Properties of Logarithms

Solutions

1. Solve: $4^x = 12$

$$\log 4^x = \log 12$$

$$x \log 4 = \log 12$$

Answer: $x = \dfrac{\log 12}{\log 4}$

Take the log of both sides, then use the power property, then divide each side by log 4.

2. Solve: $3^x = 16$

$$\log 3^x = \log 16$$

$$x \log 3 = \log 16$$

Answer: $x = \dfrac{\log 16}{\log 3}$

Take the log of both sides, then use the power property, then divide each side by log 3.

3. Solve: $2(4^x) = 28$

$$4^x = 14$$

$$\log 4^x = \log 14$$

$$x \log 4 = \log 14$$

Answer: $x = \dfrac{\log 14}{\log 4}$

Start by dividing each side by 2 to get the exponential term isolated. Then take the log of both sides, use the power property, and divide by log 4.

4. Solve: $5(2^x) = 25$

$$2^x = 5$$

$$\log 2^x = \log 5$$

$$x \log 2 = \log 5$$

Answer: $x = \dfrac{\log 5}{\log 2}$

Start by dividing each side by 5 to get the exponential term isolated. Then take the log of both sides, use the power property, and divide by log 2.

5. Solve: $3^x + 5 = 17$

$$3^x = 12$$

$$x \log 3 = \log 12$$

Answer: $x = \dfrac{\log 12}{\log 3}$

Start by subtracting 5 from each side to get the exponential term isolated. Then take the log of both sides, use the power property, and divide by log 3.

6. Solve: $4 + 3(2^x) = 19$

$$2^x = 5$$

$$x \log 2 = \log 5$$

Answer: $x = \dfrac{\log 5}{\log 2}$

To isolate the exponential term this time we have to first subtract 4 from each side and then divide by 3. Then take the log of both sides, use the power property, and divide by log 2.

7. Solve: $5^{3x-1} = 12$

$$(3x - 1) \log 5 = \log 12$$

$$3x - 1 = \frac{\log 12}{\log 5}$$

$$3x = \frac{\log 12}{\log 5} + 1$$

Answer: $x = \dfrac{\dfrac{\log 12}{\log 5} + 1}{3}$

Take the log of each side. Use the power property (even though the exponent looks a little different). Divide each side by log 5. Then add 1 to each side. Finally divide each side by the coefficient of the variable which is 3.

8. Solve: $6^{4x+5} = 16$

$$(4x + 5) \log 6 = \log 16$$

$$4x + 5 = \frac{\log 16}{\log 6}$$

$$4x = \frac{\log 16}{\log 6} - 5$$

Answer: $x = \dfrac{\dfrac{\log 16}{\log 6} - 5}{4}$

Take the log of each side. Use the power property. Divide each side by log 6. Then subtract 5 from each side. Finally divide each side by the coefficient of the variable which is 4.

9. Solve: $4^{2x+6} = 20$

$$(2x + 6) \log 4 = \log 20$$

$$2x + 6 = \frac{\log 20}{\log 4}$$

$$2x = \frac{\log 20}{\log 4} - 6$$

Answer: $x = \dfrac{\dfrac{\log 20}{\log 4} - 6}{2}$

Take the log of each side. Use the power property. Divide each side by log 4. Then subtract 6 from each side. Finally divide each side by the coefficient of the variable which is 2.

10. Solve: $3^{3x-2} = 3$

$$(3x - 2) \log 3 = \log 3$$

$$3x - 2 = \frac{\log 3}{\log 3}$$

$$3x - 2 = 1$$

$$3x = 3$$

Answer: $x = 1$

Take the log of both sides. Use the power property. Divide each side by log 3. Anything divided by itself is 1, so we have a simple linear equation to solve. Because the base on each side of the equation is the same, we could have simply set the exponent on the left to the exponent on the right and then solved.

Lesson 31: Properties of Logarithms

Lesson 32: Natural Logarithms

Now let's turn our attention to logarithms with a special base. This base is an irrational number that has been given the designation e. The value of e is approximately 2.71828. When we use this base we are using **natural logarithms** and rather than use the symbol "log" we use "ln". Just as we did with common logs, we don't write the base. When you see "ln" you know the base is e. The good news with natural logs is that all the rules that apply to "log" apply to "ln" as well.

For example, let's repeat the properties of logarithms but use natural log notation.

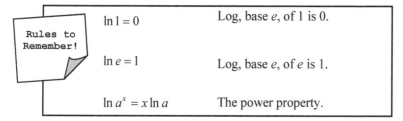

Rules to Remember!	$\ln 1 = 0$	Log, base e, of 1 is 0.
	$\ln e = 1$	Log, base e, of e is 1.
	$\ln a^x = x \ln a$	The power property.

Let's take an example from the previous lesson and solve it using natural logarithms.

Example 1.   Solve: $3^x = 18$ Take the natural log of each side.

$\ln 3^x = \ln 18$

$x \ln 3 = \ln 18$ Use the power property.

$x = \dfrac{\ln 18}{\ln 3}$ Divide each side by natural log 3.

The calculator would give us the same decimal answer as with common logs.

Here are two more problems that we will solve by using our knowledge of natural logarithms.

Example 2.   Solve: $\ln(3x) = 4$

$e^4 = 3x$ Rewrite in exponential notation.

$\dfrac{e^4}{3} = x$ Divide each side by 3.

Example 3.   Solve: $e^{2x} = 62$

$\ln 62 = 2x$ Rewrite in logarithmic notation.

$\dfrac{\ln 62}{2} = x$ Divide each side by 2.

Now it's your turn.

Lesson 32: Natural Logarithms

Lesson 32: Natural Logarithms

Exercises

1. Write in logarithmic format: $e^x = c$

2. Write in exponential format: $\ln e = 1$

3. Write in exponential format: $\ln 1 = 0$

Solve:

4. $\ln(e^5) = x$ 5. $\ln 1 = x$ 6. $\ln e = x$

7. Solve for x using natural log notation: $2(4^x) = 14$

8. Solve for x using natural log notation: $3(2^x) = 60$

9. Solve for x: $\ln(7x) = 15$

10. Solve for x: $e^{4x} = 37$

Lesson 32: Natural Logarithms

Solutions

1. Write in logarithmic format: $e^x = c$ Answer: $\ln c = x$
2. Write in exponential format: $\ln e = 1$ Answer: $e^1 = e$
3. Write in exponential format: $\ln 1 = 0$ Answer: $e^0 = 1$

Solve:

4. $\ln(e^5) = x$ Write in exponential format. When the bases are the same, the exponents must be equal.
   $e^x = e^5$
   $x = 5$

5. $\ln 1 = x$ Write in exponential format. From our properties of exponents we should know that a base raised to a 0 power is 1.
   $e^x = 1$
   $x = 0$

6. $\ln e = x$ Write in exponential format. With the same bases, the exponents must be equal.
   $e^x = e$
   $x = 1$

7. Solve for x using natural log notation:
   $$2(4^x) = 14$$
   $$4^x = 7$$
   $$\ln 4^x = \ln 7$$
   $$x \ln 4 = \ln 7$$
   Answer: $x = \dfrac{\ln 7}{\ln 4}$

   Divide each side by 2. Take the natural log of both sides. Use the power property. Divide each side by $\ln 4$.

8. Solve for x using natural log notation:
   $$3(2^x) = 60$$
   $$2^x = 20$$
   $$\ln 2^x = \ln 20$$
   $$x \ln 2 = \ln 20$$
   Answer: $x = \dfrac{\ln 20}{\ln 2}$

   Divide each side by 3. Take the natural log of both sides. Use the power property. Divide each side by $\ln 2$.

9. Solve for x: $\ln(7x) = 15$
   $$e^{15} = 7x$$
   Answer: $x = \dfrac{e^{15}}{7}$

   Rewrite in exponential notation and then divide each side by 7.

10. Solve for x: $e^{4x} = 37$
    $$\ln 37 = 4x$$
    Answer: $x = \dfrac{\ln 37}{4}$

    Rewrite in logarithmic notation and then divide each side by 4.

Lesson 33: Quadratic Functions

Although we learned about quadratic *equations* in the Elementary Algebra section, we will now look at quadratic *functions* and their graphs in this lesson and learn to identify some of the key aspects of those graphs.

Let's start by examining a simple quadratic function: $f(x) = x^2$.

To graph this function, we start by setting up our table of points and then generating the curve resulting from these points:

x	$f(x)$
-3	9
-2	4
-1	1
0	0
1	1
2	4
3	9

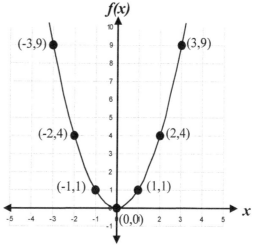

This figure is called a parabola. Notice that both positive and negative x values result in the same y value. This means that the y axis, in this case, divides the parabola in half. One side is the mirror image of the other. This is a characteristic of all parabolas. This particular parabola decreases as the x value approaches 0 from the left and then increases as the x value increases from 0 to the right. The minimum point is called the *vertex* of the parabola and a vertical line through the vertex is called the *axis of symmetry*. In this case, the axis of symmetry is the y axis or the line $x = 0$.

Now let's take a quadratic function, determine the coordinates of all intercepts, the coordinates of the vertex, the equation of the axis of symmetry, and finally, the graph of the function.

> **Example 1.** $f(x) = x^2 - 8x + 12$

Setting up a table of values may prove difficult, so let's try to find points of the parabola that will enable us to graph it without a table. First, let's find the intercepts of the function. Remember, to find the y intercept, set $x = 0$ and solve for y, and to find the x intercept, set $y = 0$ and solve for x.

Find the y intercept:

$f(0) = 0^2 - 8(0) + 12$
$f(0) = 12$

y intercept is $(0,12)$

Find the x intercept(s):

$0 = x^2 - 8x + 12$
$0 = (x - 6)(x - 2)$
$x = 6, 2$

x intercepts are: $(6,0)$ and $(2,0)$

187

Lesson 33: Quadratic Functions

We now have three important points on our parabola. Next, let's find the vertex. We can determine the vertex by using the coefficients of the x^2 term and the x term. Do you remember the standard form of a quadratic equation?

> Standard form of a quadratic equation: $ax^2 + bx + c = 0; \quad a \neq 0$
>
> **A Rule to Remember!**

The coefficient of the x^2 term is called a and the coefficient of the x term is called b. The formula for the x coordinate of the vertex is: $\dfrac{-b}{2a}$. For **Example 1**, it is: $\dfrac{-(-8)}{2(1)} = \dfrac{8}{2} = 4$. The y coordinate value of the vertex is found by substituting the x coordinate value into the original equation to find y:

$$f(4) = 4^2 - 8(4) + 12 = 16 - 32 + 12 = -4$$

The coordinates of the vertex are (4,-4). The axis of symmetry is a vertical line through the vertex, so its equation is $x = 4$. From this information we can graph this parabola as shown below:

Note that this parabola opens up so it has a *minimum* value at the vertex.

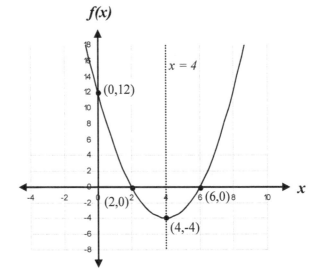

Lesson 33: Quadratic Functions

Let's look at another quadratic function.

Example 2. $f(x) = -2x^2 - 7x + 4$

Using the same process we used in **Example 1,** we will find the intercepts first, then the vertex and axis of symmetry, and then we will graph it.

Find the y intercept: $f(0) = -2(0)^2 - 7(0) + 4 = 4$ The y intercept is: $(0,4)$

Find the x intercept(s): $0 = -2x^2 - 7x + 4$

$$0 = (-2x + 1)(x + 4)$$

$$x = \frac{1}{2}, -4 \qquad \text{The } x \text{ intercepts are:} \qquad \left(\frac{1}{2}, 0\right) \text{ and } (-4, 0)$$

Find the coordinates of the vertex: The x coordinate: $x = \dfrac{-b}{2a} = \dfrac{-(-7)}{2(-2)} = -\dfrac{7}{4}$

$$\text{The } y \text{ coordinate: } f\left(-\frac{7}{4}\right) = -2\left(-\frac{7}{4}\right)^2 - 7\left(-\frac{7}{4}\right) + 4$$

$$f\left(-\frac{7}{4}\right) = -2\left(\frac{49}{16}\right) + \frac{49}{4} + 4$$

$$f\left(-\frac{7}{4}\right) = -\frac{49}{8} + \frac{98}{8} + \frac{32}{8} = \frac{81}{8} = 10\frac{1}{8}$$

The vertex is $\left(-\dfrac{7}{4}, 10\dfrac{1}{8}\right)$ and the axis of symmetry is $x = -\dfrac{7}{4}$

Plotting fractional values is very difficult but the general form of the parabola is apparent and it is different from **Example 1**. This parabola opens down so it has a *maximum* value at the vertex. It looks like this:

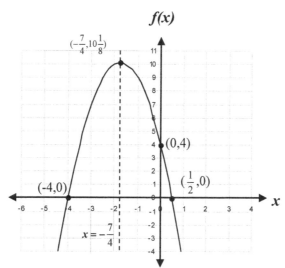

 Now it's your turn.

Lesson 33: Quadratic Functions

Lesson 33: Quadratic Functions

Exercises

1. For the function $f(x) = x^2 - 12x + 20$:

    a. Find the x intercept(s).

    b. Find the y intercept.

    c. Find the coordinates of the vertex.

    d. Find the axis of symmetry.

    e. Sketch the graph of the function.

    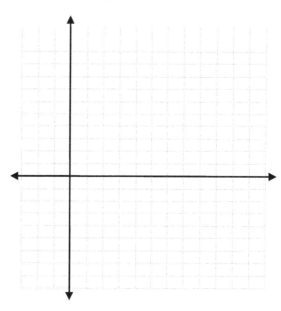

2. For the function $g(x) = -x^2 + 10x - 24$:

    a. Find the x intercept(s).

    b. Find the y intercept.

    c. Find the coordinates of the vertex.

    d. Find the axis of symmetry.

    e. Sketch the graph of the function.

    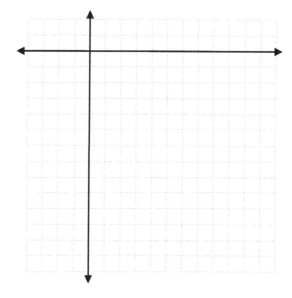

3. For the function $h(x) = -x^2 - 12x - 37$:

    a. Find the x intercept(s).

    b. Find the y intercept.

    c. Find the coordinates of the vertex.

    d. Find the axis of symmetry.

    e. Sketch the graph of the function.

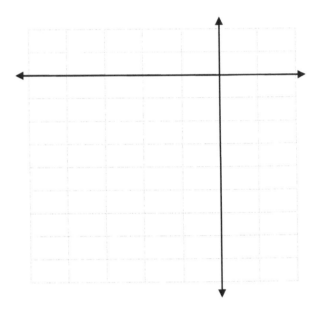

Lesson 33: Quadratic Functions

Solutions

1. For the function $f(x) = x^2 - 12x + 20$:

a. Find the x intercept(s):
   Set $y = 0$ and solve for x.
   $$0 = x^2 - 12x + 20$$
   $$(x - 10)(x - 2) = 0$$
   $$x = 10, 2$$
   Answer: x intercepts are: (10,0) and (2,0)

b. Find the y intercept:
   Set $x = 0$ and solve for y.
   $$y = 0^2 - 12(0) + 20$$
   $$y = 20$$
   Answer: y intercept: (0,20)

c. Find the coordinates of the vertex:
   The x coordinate is: $\dfrac{-b}{2a} = \dfrac{-(-12)}{2(1)} = 6$

   The y coordinate is:
   $$f(6) = 6^2 - 12(6) + 20 = 36 - 72 + 20 = -16$$
   Answer: The coordinates of the vertex are: (6,-16)

d. Find the axis of symmetry:

Answer: The equation of the vertical line through the vertex is: $x = 6$

e. Sketch the graph of the function:

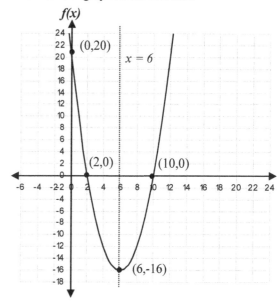

2. For the function $g(x) = -x^2 + 10x - 24$:

a. Find the x intercept(s):
   Set $y = 0$ and solve for x.
   $$0 = -x^2 + 10x - 24$$
   $$(-x + 4)(x - 6) = 0$$
   $$x = 4, 6$$
   Answer: x intercepts: (4,0) and (6,0)

b. Find the y intercept:
   Set $x = 0$ and solve for y.
   $$y = -0^2 + 10(0) - 24$$
   $$y = -24$$
   Answer: y intercept are: (0,-24)

e. Sketch the graph of the function:

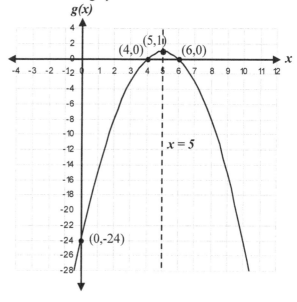

193

c. Find the coordinates of the vertex:

The x coordinate is: $\dfrac{-b}{2a} = \dfrac{-10}{2(-1)} = \dfrac{-10}{-2} = 5$

The y coordinate is: $g(5) = -(5)^2 + 10(5) - 24 = -25 + 50 - 24 = 1$

Answer: The coordinates of the vertex are: $(5,1)$

d. Find the axis of symmetry:

Answer: The equation of the vertical line through the vertex is: $x = 5$

3.   For the function $h(x) = -x^2 - 12x - 37$:

a. Find the x intercept(s):
    Set $y = 0$ and solve for x.
    We need to use the quadratic formula to solve this.

Answer: Since the radicand is negative, we don't have any real solutions. This means there is no x intercept.

$$\dfrac{-(-12) \pm \sqrt{(-12)^2 - 4(-1)(-37)}}{2(-1)} = \dfrac{12 \pm \sqrt{144 - 148}}{-2} = \dfrac{12 \pm \sqrt{-4}}{-2}$$

b. Find the y intercept:
    Set $x = 0$ and solve for y.

$y = -0^2 - 12(0) - 37$

$y = -37$

Answer: y intercept: $(0,-37)$

e.   Sketch the graph of the function:

c. Find the coordinates of the vertex:

The x coordinate is: $\dfrac{-b}{2a} = \dfrac{-(-12)}{2(-1)} = -6$

The y coordinate is:

$h(-6) = -(-6)^2 - 12(-6) - 37 = -36 + 72 - 37 = -1$

Answer: The coordinates of the vertex are: $(-6,-1)$

d. Find the axis of symmetry:
Answer: $x = -6$

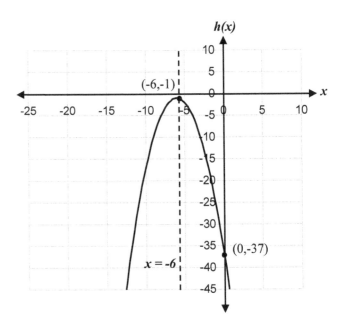

Lesson 34: Complex Numbers

Mathematicians are famous for creating symbols or systems to represent something in order to make things simpler (we hope!). For example, we use exponents rather than repeated multiplication. We use logarithms to represent inverses of exponential expressions. We use the symbol π to help us do calculations involving circles. Now we are going to use another symbol, i, to represent $\sqrt{-1}$. We use this symbol to help us express any radical that contains a negative number.

Example 1. Express $\sqrt{-4}$ using the symbol i.

$$\sqrt{-4} = \sqrt{4}\sqrt{-1} = 2i$$

Example 2. Express $\sqrt{-49}$ using the symbol i.

$$\sqrt{-49} = \sqrt{49}\sqrt{-1} = 7i$$

Example 3. Express $\sqrt{-23}$ using the symbol i.

$$\sqrt{-23} = \sqrt{23}\sqrt{-1} = \sqrt{23}i \quad \text{Note that the } i \text{ is not under the radical sign.}$$

Example 4. Express $\sqrt{-48}$ using the symbol i.

$$\sqrt{-48} = \sqrt{48}\sqrt{-1} = \sqrt{16}\sqrt{3}\sqrt{-1} = 4\sqrt{3}i$$

These expressions using the symbol i are called *imaginary* numbers. We can combine real numbers and imaginary numbers to form *complex* numbers of the form $a + bi$. Here are some examples of complex numbers:

$$3 + 4i \qquad\qquad 2 - 5i \qquad\qquad \frac{1}{2} \pm \frac{\sqrt{5}}{4}i$$

Let's practice using the complex number form.

Example 5. Write the following as a complex number: $\dfrac{5 + \sqrt{-23}}{2}$

In this example, we have two terms in the numerator and one in the denominator. That means each term in the numerator is divided by the denominator. We also have to take care of the negative radicand. Here is how it looks:

$$\frac{5 + \sqrt{-23}}{2} = \frac{5}{2} + \frac{\sqrt{23}}{2}i$$

Example 6. Write the following as a complex number in simplest form: $\dfrac{4 \pm \sqrt{-27}}{6}$

After we write this as a complex number, let's put it in it's simplest form (i.e. reduce fractions!).

$$\frac{4 \pm \sqrt{-27}}{6} = \frac{4}{6} \pm \frac{\sqrt{27}}{6}i = \frac{2}{3} \pm \frac{3\sqrt{3}}{6}i = \frac{2}{3} \pm \frac{\sqrt{3}}{2}i$$

Lesson 34: Complex Numbers

In lesson 19, we solved quadratic equations using the quadratic formula. Remember?

$$\text{If } ax^2 + bx + c = 0, \ a \neq 0, \text{ then}$$
$$x = \frac{-b \pm \sqrt{b^2 - 4ac}}{2a}$$

In those problems we always had a positive radicand (the expression under the radical sign). Now, using the new symbol i, we can express the answer to a quadratic equation even if we have a negative radicand.

Example 7. Solve: $3x^2 + 3x + 5 = 0$ Write the answer as a complex number in simplest form.

Using the quadratic formula: $x = \dfrac{-3 \pm \sqrt{9 - 4(3)(5)}}{2(3)} = \dfrac{-3 \pm \sqrt{-51}}{6} = -\dfrac{3}{6} \pm \dfrac{\sqrt{51}}{6}i = -\dfrac{1}{2} \pm \dfrac{\sqrt{51}}{6}i$

Example 8. Solve: $3x^2 - 4x + 4 = 0$ Write the answer as a complex number in simplest form.

$$x = \frac{-(-4) \pm \sqrt{16 - 4(3)(4)}}{2(3)} = \frac{4 \pm \sqrt{-32}}{6} = \frac{2}{3} \pm \frac{\sqrt{32}}{6}i = \frac{2}{3} \pm \frac{4\sqrt{2}}{6}i = \frac{2}{3} \pm \frac{2\sqrt{2}}{3}i$$

Now it's your turn.

Lesson 34: Complex Numbers

Exercises

1. Express the following as a complex number: $\dfrac{3-\sqrt{-23}}{2}$

2. Express the following as a complex number: $\dfrac{5+\sqrt{-17}}{4}$

3. Express the following as a complex number: $\dfrac{6\pm\sqrt{-14}}{5}$

4. Express the following as a complex number in simplest form: $\dfrac{-4+\sqrt{-48}}{2}$

5. Express the following as a complex number in simplest form: $\dfrac{3\pm\sqrt{-81}}{6}$

6. Solve and write the answer as a complex number in simplest form: $x^2+4x+6=0$

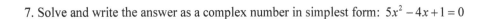
7. Solve and write the answer as a complex number in simplest form: $5x^2 - 4x + 1 = 0$

8. Solve and write the answer as a complex number in simplest form: $3x^2 + 8x = -7$

9. Solve and write the answer as a complex number in simplest form: $x^2 - 4x + 13 = 0$

Lesson 34: Complex Numbers

Solutions

1. Express the following as a complex number: $\dfrac{3-\sqrt{-23}}{2}$ Answer: $\dfrac{3}{2}-\dfrac{\sqrt{23}}{2}i$

2. Express the following as a complex number: $\dfrac{5+\sqrt{-17}}{4}$ Answer: $\dfrac{5}{4}+\dfrac{\sqrt{17}}{4}i$

3. Express the following as a complex number: $\dfrac{6\pm\sqrt{-14}}{5}$ Answer: $\dfrac{6}{5}\pm\dfrac{\sqrt{14}}{5}i$

4. Express the following as a complex number in simplest form: $\dfrac{-4+\sqrt{-48}}{2}$

Answer: $\dfrac{-4+\sqrt{-48}}{2}=\dfrac{-4}{2}+\dfrac{\sqrt{48}}{2}i=-2+\dfrac{4\sqrt{3}}{2}i=-2+2\sqrt{3}i$

5. Express the following as a complex number in simplest form: $\dfrac{3\pm\sqrt{-81}}{6}$

Answer: $\dfrac{3\pm\sqrt{-81}}{6}=\dfrac{3}{6}\pm\dfrac{9}{6}i=\dfrac{1}{2}\pm\dfrac{3}{2}i$

6. Solve and write the answer as a complex number in simplest form: $x^2+4x+6=0$

Use the quadratic formula to solve for x:

Answer: $x=\dfrac{-4\pm\sqrt{16-4(1)(6)}}{2(1)}=\dfrac{-4\pm\sqrt{-8}}{2}=\dfrac{-4}{2}\pm\dfrac{\sqrt{8}}{2}i=-2\pm\dfrac{2\sqrt{2}}{2}i=-2\pm\sqrt{2}i$

7. Solve and write the answer as a complex number in simplest form: $5x^2 - 4x + 1 = 0$

Use the quadratic formula to solve for x:

Answer: $x = \dfrac{-(-4) \pm \sqrt{16 - 4(5)(1)}}{10} = \dfrac{4 \pm \sqrt{-4}}{10} = \dfrac{4}{10} \pm \dfrac{2}{10}i = \dfrac{2}{5} \pm \dfrac{1}{5}i$

8. Solve and write the answer as a complex number in simplest form: $3x^2 + 8x = -7$
First put this equation in the standard form of a quadratic equation: $3x^2 + 8x + 7 = 0$, then use the quadratic formula to solve for x:

Answer: $x = \dfrac{-8 \pm \sqrt{64 - 4(3)(7)}}{6} = \dfrac{-8 \pm \sqrt{-20}}{6} = \dfrac{-4}{3} \pm \dfrac{2\sqrt{5}}{6}i = -\dfrac{4}{3} \pm \dfrac{\sqrt{5}}{3}i$

9. Solve and write the answer as a complex number in simplest form: $x^2 - 4x + 13 = 0$
Use the quadratic formula to solve for x:

Answer: $x = \dfrac{-(-4) \pm \sqrt{16 - 4(1)(13)}}{2(1)} = \dfrac{4 \pm \sqrt{-36}}{2} = \dfrac{4}{2} \pm \dfrac{\sqrt{36}}{2}i = 2 \pm 3i$

Lesson 35: Solving Non-Linear Systems of Equations

Back in lessons 14, 15, and 16, we solved systems of *linear* equations in two variables in three ways: graphing, substitution, and elimination. Now we will use substitution and elimination in solving *non-linear* systems of equations. We could also use graphing but as we learned in lesson 14, graphing the intersection of two lines was not very accurate and very difficult if fractions were involved. It would be even harder with non-linear systems. Remember that the solution for a system of equations in two variables is a point of intersection. So, if a non linear system of equations in two variables has a solution, it will be one or more ordered pairs in the form (x, y).

Consider this system of equations:

Example 1.
$$\text{Solve: } y = x^2 + 1$$
$$y = 3 - x$$

We will use the substitution method to solve this system of equations. We will use the value of y in the second equation $(3 - x)$ to substitute for the value of y in the first equation. This will result in an equation with one unknown (x). After we solve for x, we will substitute that value back into one of the equations (either one is OK) to find the value or values of the y coordinate. Here goes:

$$3 - x = x^2 + 1 \qquad \text{Substitute } 3 - x \text{ for } y \text{ in the first equation.}$$
$$0 = x^2 + x - 2 \qquad \text{Put the resulting quadratic equation in}$$
$$0 = (x + 2)(x - 1) \qquad \text{standard form and solve.}$$
$$x = 1, -2$$

Now solve for y, when $x = 1$ $\qquad y = 3 - 1 = 2$ This solution is: (1,2)

Now solve for y, when $x = -2$ $\qquad y = 3 - (-2) = 5$ This solution is: (-2,5)

So, for this system of equations, there are two points of intersection: (1,2) and (-2,5).

Example 2.
$$\text{Solve: } x^2 + y^2 = 4$$
$$x^2 + 4y^2 = 16$$

We will use the elimination method for solving this system of equations. Subtract the second equation from the first and then solve for y.

$$x^2 + y^2 = 4 \qquad\qquad \text{Multiply the second equation by } -1 \text{ and then}$$
$$\underline{-x^2 - 4y^2 = -16} \qquad \text{add the equations.}$$
$$-3y^2 = -12 \qquad\qquad \text{Divide each side by } -3.$$
$$y^2 = 4$$
$$y = \pm 2 \qquad\qquad \text{Take the square root of each side.}$$

Now substitute each y value into one of the equations and solve for x.

For $y = 2$: $\quad x^2 + (2)^2 = 4 \qquad$ For $y = -2$: $\quad x^2 + (-2)^2 = 4$

$$x^2 + 4 = 4 \qquad\qquad\qquad x^2 + 4 = 4$$
$$x^2 = 0 \qquad\qquad\qquad\qquad x^2 = 0$$
$$x = 0 \qquad\qquad\qquad\qquad x = 0$$

The two points of intersection (the solution) are: (0,2) and (0,-2).

201

Lesson 35: Solving Non-Linear Systems of Equations

Example 3.
Solve: $x^2 + 2y^2 = 41$
$3x^2 - y^2 = 11$

Let's use the elimination method for this problem. The first step will be to multiply the second equation by 2 and then add the two equations. That will eliminate the y^2 term. We can then find the value for x and substitute that value or values back into one of the equations to find the value for y. Let's see how many points of intersection we have for this problem.

$$x^2 + 2y^2 = 41$$
$$\underline{6x^2 - 2y^2 = 22}$$

Multiply the second equation by 2 and add the two equations.

$$7x^2 = 63$$
$$x^2 = 9$$

Divide each side by 7.

$$x = \pm 3$$

Take the square root of each side.

Substitute $x = 3$ and solve for y:
$$(3)^2 + 2y^2 = 41$$
$$9 + 2y^2 = 41$$
$$2y^2 = 32$$
$$y^2 = 16$$
$$y = \pm 4$$

This results in two points of intersection: (3,4) and (3,-4)

Substitute $x = -3$ and solve for y:
$$(-3)^2 + 2y^2 = 41$$
$$9 + 2y^2 = 41$$
$$2y^2 = 32$$
$$y^2 = 16$$
$$y = \pm 4$$

This results in two **more** points of intersection: (-3,4) and (-3,-4)

So, there are 4 points of intersection for these two equations: (3,4), (3,-4), (-3,4), and (-3,-4).

Now let's try to solve one more non-linear system of equations and see how many points of intersection we get.

Example 4. Solve:
$$x^2 + 4y^2 = 4$$
$$16x^2 + 25y^2 = 89$$

Solve by the elimination method. Multiply the first equation by –16 and then add the two equations.

$$-16x^2 - 64y^2 = -64$$
$$\underline{16x^2 + 25y^2 = 89}$$
$$-39y^2 = 25$$
$$y^2 = -\frac{25}{39}$$

Since there is no real number that would satisfy this equation (you can't square a number and get a negative result), there are **no** points of intersection for these two equations.

Now it's your turn.

Lesson 35: Solving Non-Linear Systems of Equations

Exercises

1. Solve the system of equations: $y = x^2 - 2$
$$y = 3x - 2$$

2. Solve the system of equations: $y = x^2 - 2x + 5$
$$y + 2x = 6$$

3. Solve the system of equations: $x^2 + y^2 = 9$
$$x^2 + 4y^2 = 36$$

4. Solve the system of equations: $x^2 + y^2 = 25$
$$4x^2 + 9y^2 = 180$$

5. Solve the system of equations: $x^2 + 4y^2 = 17$
$$6x^2 + 3y^2 = 18$$

Lesson 35: Solving Non-Linear Systems of Equations

Solutions

1. Solve the system of equations: $y = x^2 - 2$
$$y = 3x - 2$$

Solve by substitution: $3x - 2 = x^2 - 2$

$$x^2 - 3x = 0$$
$$x(x - 3) = 0$$
$$x = 0, 3$$

Substitute the value of y in the second equation for the value of y in the first equation and solve the resulting quadratic equation for x.

When $x = 0$: $y = 3(0) - 2$
$$y = -2$$

Substitute $x = 0$ into either equation and solve for y.

When $x = 3$: $y = 3(3) - 2$
$$y = 7$$

Substitute $x = 3$ into either equation and solve for y.

Answer: There are two points of intersection: $\quad$ (0,-2) and (3,7)

2. Solve the system of equations: $\quad y = x^2 - 2x + 5$
$$y + 2x = 6$$

Solve by substitution: $6 - 2x = x^2 - 2x + 5$

$$x^2 - 1 = 0$$
$$(x + 1)(x - 1) = 0$$
$$x = 1, -1$$

Solve the second equation for y and then substitute that value of y for the value of y in the first equation and solve the resulting quadratic equation for x.

An alternative way would be to take the value of y in the first equation and substitute it for the value of y in the second equation. The answer will be the same.

When $x = 1$: $y + 2(1) = 6$
$$y = 4$$

Substitute $x = 1$ into either equation and solve for y.

When $x = -1$: $y + 2(-1) = 6$
$$y = 8$$

Substitute $x = -1$ into either equation and solve for y.

Answer: There are two points of intersection : $\quad$ (1,4) and (-1,8)

3. Solve the system of equations: $x^2 + y^2 = 9$

$$x^2 + 4y^2 = 36$$

Solve by elimination: $\quad -x^2 - y^2 = -9$

$$\underline{\quad x^2 + 4y^2 = 36 \quad}$$

$$3y^2 = 27$$

$$y^2 = 9$$

$$y = \pm 3$$

Multiply the first equation by -1, then add the two equations to eliminate the x variable. Solve the resulting quadratic equation.

When $y = 3$: $\quad x^2 + 3^2 = 9$

$$x^2 + 9 = 9$$

$$x^2 = 0$$

$$x = 0$$

Substitute $y = 3$ into either equation and solve for x.

When $y = -3$: $\quad x^2 + (-3)^2 = 9$

$$x^2 + 9 = 9$$

$$x = 0$$

Substitute $y = $ -3 into either equation and solve for x.

Answer: There are two points of intersection: $\qquad$ (0,3) and (0,-3)

4. Solve the system of equations: $x^2 + y^2 = 25$

$$4x^2 + 9y^2 = 180$$

Solve by elimination: $\quad -4x^2 - 4y^2 = -100$

$$\underline{\quad 4x^2 + 9y^2 = 180 \quad}$$

$$5y^2 = 80$$

$$y^2 = 16$$

$$y = \pm 4$$

Multiply the first equation by -4, then add the two equations to eliminate the x variable. Solve the resulting quadratic equation.

When $y = 4$: $\quad x^2 + 4^2 = 25$

$$x^2 = 9$$

$$x = \pm 3$$

Substitute $y = 4$ into either equation and solve for x.

When $y = -4$: $\quad x^2 + (-4)^2 = 25$

$$x^2 = 9$$

$$x = \pm 3$$

Substitute $y = $ -4 into either equation and solve for x.

Answer: There are four points of intersection: $\qquad$ (3,4), (3.-4), (-3,4) and (-3,-4)

5. Solve the system of equations: $x^2 + 4y^2 = 17$

$$6x^2 + 3y^2 = 18$$

Solve by elimination:

$$-6x^2 - 24y^2 = -102$$
$$6x^2 + 3y^2 = 18$$
$$\overline{}$$
$$-21y^2 = -84$$
$$y^2 = 4$$
$$y = \pm 2$$

Multiply the first equation by -6, then add the two equations to eliminate the x variable. Divide each side by -21. Solve the resulting quadratic equation.

When $y = 2$: $x^2 + 4(2)^2 = 17$

$$x^2 + 16 = 17$$
$$x^2 = 1$$
$$x = \pm 1$$

Substitute $y = 2$ into either equation and solve for x.

When $y = -2$: $x^2 + 4(-2)^2 = 17$

$$x^2 + 16 = 17$$
$$x^2 = 1$$
$$x = \pm 1$$

Substitute $y = -2$ into either equation and solve for x.

Answer: There are four points of intersection: $(1,2)$, $(1,-2)$, $(-1,2)$, and $(-1,-2)$

Lesson 35: Solving Non-Linear Systems of Equations

Lesson 36: Rational Functions

We learned about rational *expressions* in lessons 11, 12, and 13, and now we are going to look at rational *functions*. A rational function has a polynomial in the numerator and also a polynomial in the denominator. Here are some examples:

$$f(x) = \frac{x+5}{x-3} \qquad\qquad g(x) = \frac{2x-7}{x} \qquad\qquad h(x) = \frac{3x-4}{x^2-3x+4}$$

Before we begin the discussion of rational functions, let's consider some new words for our English-Algebra dictionary – the words *Domain* and *Range*. Domain is the set of all valid input (or *x*) values and range is the set of all valid output (or *y*) values. Let's consider some examples.

Example 1. What is the domain and range for: $f(x) = x+5$?

For any linear function, there is no restriction on the values of *x* or *y* so the domain is the set of all real numbers and so is the range.

This is not the case for a rational function, or as we will learn in the lesson 38, radical functions.

Example 2. What is the domain and range for: $f(x) = \frac{4}{x-3}$

When we have a rational function, there may be value(s) of *x* that will cause the denominator to become zero which would make the function undefined. Therefore, we must exclude any such values from the domain. In Example 2, the value of *x* that would make the denominator zero is 3. So, the domain is the set of all real numbers except $x = 3$. The range for this example is not restricted. We will revisit range in the next lesson. For now, let's just concentrate on finding the *domain* of rational functions.

Example 3. Find the domain of: $f(x) = \frac{x-6}{x+4}$

To find the value (or values) to exclude from the domain, simply set the denominator equal to 0 and solve for *x*.

$$x+4 = 0$$
$$x = -4$$

The domain is the set of all real numbers **except** *x* = -4.

Example 4. Find the domain of: $g(x) = \frac{2x+3}{4x-8}$

$$4x-8 = 0$$
$$4x = 8$$
$$x = 2$$

The domain is the set of all real numbers **except** *x* = 2.

Example 5. Find the domain of: $h(x) = \frac{x-7}{x^2+7x+10}$

$$x^2+7x+10 = 0$$
$$(x+2)(x+5) = 0$$
$$x = -2, -5$$

The domain is the set of all real numbers **except** *x* = -2 and *x* = -5.

Simplifying Rational Functions

Now let's look at simplifying a rational function. The process is the same as simplifying fractions, in that we look for common factors in the numerator and denominator.

Example 6.   Simplify: $f(x) = \dfrac{4x-12}{8x-24}$

$f(x) = \dfrac{4(x-3)}{4 \bullet 2(x-3)}$ Factor numerator and denominator, then cancel common factors.

$f(x) = \dfrac{1}{2}$

Example 7.   Simplify: $g(x) = \dfrac{x^2-5x}{x^2-7x+10}$

$g(x) = \dfrac{x(x-5)}{(x-5)(x-2)}$ Factor numerator and denominator, then cancel common factors.

$g(x) = \dfrac{x}{x-2}$

Now let's find the domain of **Example 7**. The question is now which denominator do we set to 0 to find values to exclude from the domain. Do we use the original function, the simplified function, or either one? The answer is: use the original function!

$$x^2 - 7x + 10 = 0$$
$$(x-5)(x-2) = 0$$ The domain is the set of all real
$$x = 5, 2$$ numbers **except** $x = 5$ and $x = 2$.

Example 8.   Simplify and find the domain of: $h(x) = \dfrac{x^2-5x-14}{x^2-10x+21}$

$h(x) = \dfrac{(x+2)(x-7)}{(x-3)(x-7)}$ Factor numerator and denominator, then cancel common factors.

$h(x) = \dfrac{x+2}{x-3}$ This is the simplified form of the function.

Find the domain: $x^2 - 10x + 21 = 0$ Set the denominator equal to 0 and solve.
$$(x-3)(x-7) = 0$$
$$x = 3, 7$$ The domain is the set of all real numbers **except** $x = 3$ and $x = 7$.

Now it's your turn ➡

210

Lesson 36: Rational Functions

Exercises

1. Find the domain of: $f(x) = \dfrac{x+7}{x-5}$

2. Find the domain of: $g(x) = \dfrac{x^2-4}{x+6}$

3. Find the domain of: $h(x) = \dfrac{x+7}{x^2+7x+12}$

4. Find the domain of: $j(x) = \dfrac{x-3}{x^2-5x}$

5. Find the domain of: $k(x) = \dfrac{x+8}{x^2-x-30}$

6. Simplify: $f(x) = \dfrac{2x+4}{x^2+7x+10}$

7. Simplify: $g(x) = \dfrac{x^2+x-6}{x^2+5x+6}$

8. Simplify: $h(x) = \dfrac{2x-14}{2x^2-10x-28}$

9. Simplify and find the domain of: $j(x) = \dfrac{x^2-5x-24}{x^2+8x+15}$

10. Simplify and find the domain of: $f(x) = \dfrac{x^2+3x-28}{x^3+13x^2+42x}$

Solutions

1. Find the domain of: $f(x) = \dfrac{x+7}{x-5}$

$x - 5 = 0$ Set the denominator equal to 0 and solve for x.

$x = 5$ This value must be excluded from the domain.

Answer: The domain is the set of all real numbers except $x = 5$.

2. Find the domain of: $g(x) = \dfrac{x^2 - 4}{x+6}$

$x + 6 = 0$ Set the denominator equal to 0 and solve for x.

$x = -6$ This value must be excluded from the domain.

Answer: The domain is the set of all real numbers except $x = -6$.

3. Find the domain of: $h(x) = \dfrac{x+7}{x^2 + 7x + 12}$

$x^2 + 7x + 12 = 0$ Set the denominator equal to 0 and solve for x by factoring

$(x+3)(x+4) = 0$ the quadratic and then using the principle of zero products.

$x = -3, -4$ These values must be excluded from the domain.

Answer: The domain is the set of all real numbers except $x = -3$ and -4.

4. Find the domain of: $j(x) = \dfrac{x-3}{x^2 - 5x}$

$x^2 - 5x = 0$ Set the denominator equal to 0 and solve for x by factoring

$x(x-5) = 0$ the quadratic and then using the principle of zero products.

$x = 0, 5$ These values must be excluded from the domain.

Answer: The domain is the set of all real numbers except $x = 0$ and 5.

5. Find the domain of: $k(x) = \dfrac{x+8}{x^2 - x - 30}$

$x^2 - x - 30 = 0$ Set the denominator equal to 0 and solve for x by factoring the

$(x-6)(x+5) = 0$ quadratic and then using the principle of zero products. These

$x = 6, -5$ values must be excluded from the domain.

Answer: The domain is the set of all real numbers except $x = 6$ and -5.

Lesson 36: Rational Functions

6. Simplify: $f(x) = \dfrac{2x+4}{x^2+7x+10} = \dfrac{2(x+2)}{(x+2)(x+5)} = \dfrac{2}{(x+5)}$ Factor the numerator and the denominator and then cancel out the common factor $x + 2$.

7. Simplify: $g(x) = \dfrac{x^2+x-6}{x^2+5x+6} = \dfrac{(x+3)(x-2)}{(x+3)(x+2)} = \dfrac{x-2}{x+2}$ Factor the numerator and the denominator and then cancel out the common factor $x + 3$.

8. Simplify: $h(x) = \dfrac{2x-14}{2x^2-10x-28} = \dfrac{2(x-7)}{2(x-7)(x+2)} = \dfrac{1}{x+2}$

Remember to factor completely! The denominator has three factors. When canceling out the common factors [2 and $(x - 7)$], the numerator's factors have all been cancelled. This leaves 1 in the numerator.

9. Simplify and find the domain of: $j(x) = \dfrac{x^2-5x-24}{x^2+8x+15} = \dfrac{(x-8)(x+3)}{(x+5)(x+3)} = \dfrac{x-8}{x+5}$ Factor the numerator and the denominator and then cancel out the common factor $x + 3$.

To determine the domain, we set the **<u>original</u>** denominator equal to 0, and solve for x.

$$x^2+8x+15 = 0$$
$$(x+5)(x+3) = 0$$
$$x = -5, -3$$

The domain is the set of all real numbers except $x =$ -5 and -3.

10. Simplify and find the domain of: $f(x) = \dfrac{x^2+3x-28}{x^3+13x^2+42x} = \dfrac{(x+7)(x-4)}{x(x+6)(x+7)} = \dfrac{x-4}{x(x+6)}$ Factor the numerator and the denominator and then cancel out the common factor $x + 7$.

To determine the domain, we set the **<u>original</u>** denominator equal to 0, and solve for x.

$$x^3+13x^2+42x = 0$$
$$x(x+6)(x+7) = 0$$
$$x = 0, -6, -7$$

The domain is the set of all real numbers except $x =$ 0, -6 and -7.

Lesson 37: Solving Rational Equations

Now let's look at how we solve rational equations. The main thing you need to remember when solving rational equations is to follow all the rules we used in solving equations with fractions. When solving equations with fractions, we found the Least Common Denominator (LCD) and multiplied every term in the equation by that number. This eliminated the fractions and resulted in an easier problem. Let's see how we can apply this process to solving rational equations.

Example 1. Solve: $5 + \dfrac{6}{x} = 8 - \dfrac{12}{x}$

The only denominator in this equation is x, so that is the LCD.

$$5 \bullet x + \dfrac{6}{x} \bullet x = 8 \bullet x - \dfrac{12}{x} \bullet x$$

Multiply by the LCD, x.

$$5x + 6 = 8x - 12$$
$$-3x = -18$$
$$x = 6$$

After multiplying by the LCD, you should not have any fractions (or rational terms) left. If you do, you better start over.

With rational equations, it is very important to check your answer. Sometimes, even though we follow the proper rules for solving equations, the answer may not check. When that happens, we call the solution extraneous. So, let's check **Example 1**:

$$5 + \dfrac{6}{x} = 8 - \dfrac{12}{x}$$
$$5 + \dfrac{6}{6} = 8 - \dfrac{12}{6}$$
$$5 + 1 = 8 - 2$$
$$6 = 6$$

 This answer checks.

Example 2. Solve: $3 - \dfrac{1}{x-3} = \dfrac{x-4}{x-3}$

The LCD in this case is $x - 3$ so we will multiply every term by that binomial.

$$3(x-3) - 1 = x - 4$$
$$3x - 9 - 1 = x - 4$$
$$2x = 6$$
$$x = 3$$

When we check this answer, we get division by 0. So, $x = 3$ is not a solution for this equation and we say we have an **empty set solution**.

Example 3. Solve: $\dfrac{x}{x-4} + \dfrac{2}{x-5} = \dfrac{2}{x^2-9x+20}$

To find the LCD, factor the denominator on the right side of the equation. Then you'll see that the LCD is that denominator since the denominators on the left side are factors of the denominator on the right side.

$$x(x-5) + 2(x-4) = 2 \qquad \text{Multiply by } (x-5)(x-4)$$
$$x^2 - 5x + 2x - 8 = 2$$
$$x^2 - 3x - 10 = 0 \qquad \text{Solve the resulting quadratic equation.}$$
$$(x-5)(x+2) = 0$$
$$x = 5, -2$$

Now, check the answers for **Example 3**:

Check $x = 5$ $\qquad \dfrac{x}{x-4} + \dfrac{2}{x-5} = \dfrac{2}{x^2-9x+20}$

$$\dfrac{5}{5-4} + \dfrac{2}{5-5} = \dfrac{2}{25-45+20}$$

$$\dfrac{5}{1} + \dfrac{2}{0} = \dfrac{2}{0}$$

This value is not valid since it results in division by 0.

Check $x = -2$ $\qquad \dfrac{x}{x-4} + \dfrac{2}{x-5} = \dfrac{2}{x^2-9x+20}$

$$\dfrac{-2}{-2-4} + \dfrac{2}{-2-5} = \dfrac{2}{4+18+20}$$

$$\dfrac{-2}{-6} + \dfrac{2}{-7} = \dfrac{2}{42}$$

$$\dfrac{14}{42} - \dfrac{12}{42} = \dfrac{2}{42}$$

$$\dfrac{2}{42} = \dfrac{2}{42}$$

✔ This value checks and is the only valid solution.

Now it's your turn.

216

Lesson 37: Solving Rational Equations

Exercises

1. Solve: $\dfrac{5}{x} + 5 = 9 - \dfrac{15}{x}$

2. Solve: $\dfrac{x}{x-2} - \dfrac{2}{x+7} = \dfrac{18}{x^2 + 5x - 14}$

3. Solve: $\dfrac{x-5}{x-8} = \dfrac{3}{x-8}$

4. Solve: $\dfrac{2}{x-2} = \dfrac{3}{x+2}$

5. Solve: $5 - \dfrac{7}{x} = \dfrac{6}{x^2}$

6. Solve: $\dfrac{8}{x^2 + x - 20} = \dfrac{4}{x+5} - \dfrac{2}{x-4}$

Lesson 37: Solving Rational Equations

Solutions

1. Solve: $\dfrac{5}{x} + 5 = 9 - \dfrac{15}{x}$

$5 + 5x = 9x - 15$

$20 = 4x$

$5 = x$

In an equation with one or more fractions, find the LCD (in this case, x) and multiply every term by that LCD. Then solve the resulting equation.

With rational equations, we <u>must</u> check our answers. It is possible to solve a rational equation and get an extraneous solution.

Check by substituting $x = 5$ back into the original equation:

$$\dfrac{5}{x} + 5 = 9 - \dfrac{15}{x}$$

$$\dfrac{5}{5} + 5 = 9 - \dfrac{15}{5}$$

$$1 + 5 = 9 - 3$$

$$6 = 6$$

This answer checks so the solution $x = 5$ is valid.

2. Solve: $\dfrac{x}{x-2} - \dfrac{2}{x+7} = \dfrac{18}{x^2 + 5x - 14}$

$x(x+7) - 2(x-2) = 18$

$x^2 + 7x - 2x + 4 = 18$

$x^2 + 5x - 14 = 0$

$(x+7)(x-2) = 0$

$x = -7, 2$

In an equation with one or more fractions, find the LCD (in this case, $(x + 7)(x - 2)$ and multiply every term by that LCD. Then solve the resulting equation.

Check by substituting $x = $ -7 and 2 back into the original equation. When we do that, we can see that each solution causes a denominator in the equation to become 0. Therefore, we have an equation with an **empty set solution** (no valid answers).

Lesson 37: Solving Rational Equations

3. Solve: $\dfrac{x-5}{x-8} = \dfrac{3}{x-8}$

$x - 5 = 3$

$x = 8$

The LCD is $x - 8$ and the resulting equation is easily solved. When you check your answer, you find a denominator of zero; therefore, we have an empty set solution.

4. Solve: $\dfrac{2}{x-2} = \dfrac{3}{x+2}$

$2(x+2) = 3(x-2)$

$2x + 4 = 3x - 6$

$10 = x$

The LCD is $(x-2)(x+2)$ and the resulting linear equation is easily solved.

Check $x = 10$:

$$\dfrac{2}{x-2} = \dfrac{3}{x+2}$$

$$\dfrac{2}{10-2} = \dfrac{3}{10+2}$$

$$\dfrac{2}{8} = \dfrac{3}{12}$$

$$\dfrac{1}{4} = \dfrac{1}{4}$$

The answer checks so the solution $x = 10$ is valid.

5. Solve: $5 - \dfrac{7}{x} = \dfrac{6}{x^2}$

$5x^2 - 7x = 6$

$5x^2 - 7x - 6 = 0$

$(5x + 3)(x - 2) = 0$

$x = 2, -\dfrac{3}{5}$

The LCD in this equation is x^2 and the resulting equation is a quadratic. Put it in the standard form of a quadratic and use the principle of zero products to solve.

Check $x = -\dfrac{3}{5}$:

$$5 - \dfrac{7}{\left(-\dfrac{3}{5}\right)} = \dfrac{6}{\left(-\dfrac{3}{5}\right)^2}$$

$$5 + \dfrac{35}{3} = \dfrac{150}{9}$$

$$\dfrac{45}{9} + \dfrac{105}{9} = \dfrac{150}{9}$$

$$\dfrac{150}{9} = \dfrac{150}{9}$$

So, $x = -\dfrac{3}{5}$ is a valid answer.

Check $x = 2$:

$$5 - \dfrac{7}{2} = \dfrac{6}{2^2}$$

$$\dfrac{10}{2} - \dfrac{7}{2} = \dfrac{6}{4}$$

$$\dfrac{3}{2} = \dfrac{3}{2}$$

So, $x = 2$ is a valid answer.

6. Solve:

$$\frac{8}{x^2 + x - 20} = \frac{4}{x+5} - \frac{2}{x-4}$$

$$8 = 4(x-4) - 2(x+5)$$

$$8 = 4x - 16 - 2x - 10$$

$$34 = 2x$$

$$17 = x$$

The first denominator is the LCD. The resulting equation is a linear equation.

Check $x = 17$:

$$\frac{8}{17^2 + 17 - 20} = \frac{4}{17+5} - \frac{2}{17-4}$$

$$\frac{8}{286} = \frac{4}{22} - \frac{2}{13}$$

$$\frac{8}{286} = \frac{52}{286} - \frac{44}{286}$$

$$\frac{8}{286} = \frac{8}{286}$$

So, the solution $x = 17$ is valid.

Lesson 38: Radical Functions

We have already discussed many types of functions: linear, quadratic, exponential, logarithmic, and rational. The last type of function we will cover is a radical function. A radical function is a function that contains a radical. Here are some examples of radical functions:

$$f(x) = \sqrt{x} \qquad\qquad g(x) = 3\sqrt{x-4} \qquad\qquad h(x) = -2\sqrt{x+5} + 3$$

Let's take a look at what a radical function looks like by graphing one.

Example 1.   Graph: $f(x) = \sqrt{x}$

As with most graphing exercises, you should set up a table of values that represent ordered pairs that satisfy the function. This table will take a little extra effort to select values of x that will result in whole number answers for the $f(x)$ or y value.

x	$f(x)$
0	0
1	1
4	2
9	3
16	4
25	5

Notice that the x value increases very rapidly while the function value (y) goes up slowly. Also, notice that there is no negative x or y value. This results in the graph shown below.

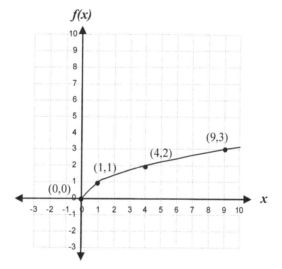

Now, let's determine the domain and range for this function. From the graph it appears that the domain (valid x values) cannot be negative. That makes sense because we can't have the square root of a negative number. The graph also indicates that the range (valid y values) also can't be negative. The reason that the negative root is not computed is that the radical symbol stands for the principal root (or non-negative) square root of x. Therefore:

The domain is the set of all numbers ≥ 0 .

The range is the set of all numbers ≥ 0 .

Lesson 38: Radical Functions

Let's look at some more radical functions. For each one, we will sketch the graph and also determine the domain and range.

Example 2.   Determine the domain and range and graph: $f(x) = \sqrt{x-3}$

Our first step will be to graph the function. We will do that by developing a table of values.

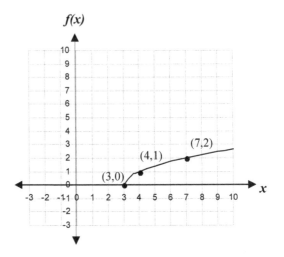

x	$f(x)$
0	$\sqrt{-3}$ (not a real number)
3	0
4	1
7	2
12	3
19	4

Note that the smallest x value that results in a valid y value is +3. Anything less than +3, results in a negative radicand.

Notice that the graph starts at the point (3,0). So, from the graph, it appears that the domain is the set of all real numbers ≥ 3. The range is the same as in the previous example: the set of all real numbers ≥ 0.

Example 3.   Determine the domain and range and graph: $f(x) = -2\sqrt{x+4} + 1$

Our table looks like this: and the graph looks like this:

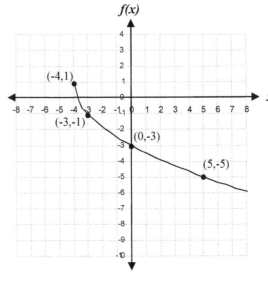

x	$f(x)$
-4	1
-3	-1
0	-3
5	-5
12	-7

From the graph, the smallest x value is –4 and the largest y value is 1. So the domain is all numbers $\geq$ -4, and the range is all real numbers ≤ 1.

Lesson 38: Radical Functions

Example 4. Determine the domain and range and graph: $f(x) = -3\sqrt{x-6} - 2$

x	$f(x)$
6	-2
7	-5
10	-8
15	-11
22	-14

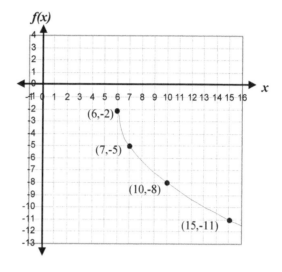

Again from the graph, the domain is the set of all real numbers ≥ 6, and the range is the set of all real numbers ≤ -2.

So far we have used the graph to try to determine what the domain and range are for each function. The following method can be used to find the domain and range directly from the rule for the function.

> For a function of the form: $f(x) = a\sqrt{radicand} + b$,
>
> the domain is the solution to: $radicand \geq 0$
>
> the range is the set of all real numbers $\geq b$ if a is positive
> or the set of all real numbers $\leq b$ if a is negative.

A Rule to Remember!

Let's see how that works in the next example which is identical to **Example 4** except that the sign of a has changed from negative to positive.

Example 5. Determine the domain and range and graph: $f(x) = 3\sqrt{x-6} - 2$

Let's first determine the domain and range algebraically.

Domain is: $radicand \geq 0$

$$x - 6 \geq 0$$
$$x \geq 6$$

The domain is the set of all real numbers ≥ 6.

Range is: The set of all real numbers ≥ -2 since a is positive.

223

Lesson 38: Radical Functions

Now; let's develop a table of values and then graph the function to see if the graph agrees with the domain and range we have just determined.

x	$f(x)$
6	-2
7	1
10	4
15	7

The graph of **Example 5** confirms our values for the domain and range.

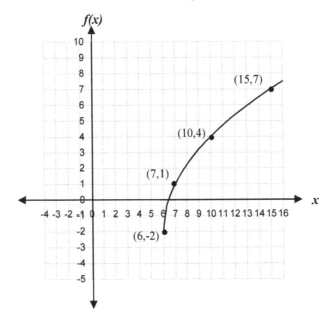

Now it's your turn. ▶

Lesson 38: Radical Functions

Exercises

1. Determine the domain and range and sketch $f(x) = 3\sqrt{x-5}$

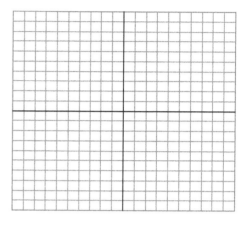

2. Determine the domain and range and sketch $g(x) = -2\sqrt{x+8}$

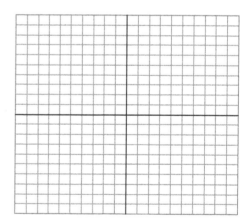

3. Determine the domain and range and sketch $h(x) = 5\sqrt{x-3} + 4$

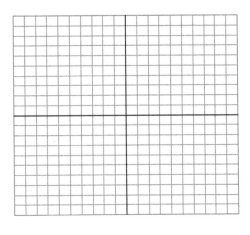

4. Determine the domain and range and sketch $j(x) = -3\sqrt{x+4} - 5$

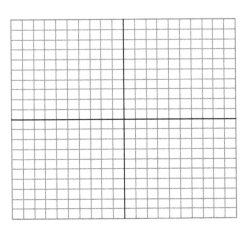

Lesson 38: Radical Functions

5. Determine the domain and range and sketch $k(x) = 3\sqrt{x} + 6$

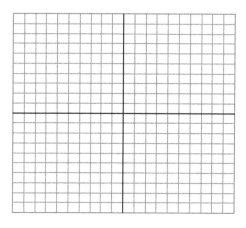

6. Determine the domain and range and sketch $l(x) = -4\sqrt{x-2} + 3$

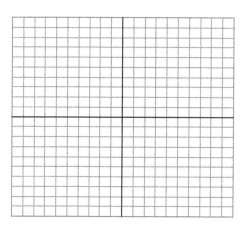

Lesson 38: Radical Functions

Solutions

1. Determine the domain and range and sketch $f(x) = 3\sqrt{x-5}$

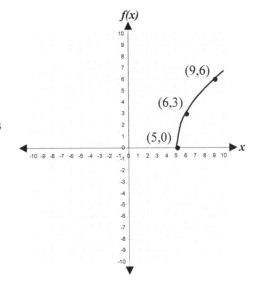

Domain: $x - 5 \geq 0$

$\quad\quad\quad x \geq 5$

Set the radicand ≥ 0 and solve. Domain is the set of all real numbers greater than or equal to 5.

Range: Since b is 0 and a is positive, the range is the set of all real numbers greater than or equal to 0.

Sketch:

x	$f(x)$
5	0
6	3
9	6
14	9

2. Determine the domain and range and sketch $g(x) = -2\sqrt{x+8}$

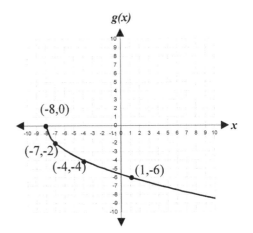

Domain: $x + 8 \geq 0$

$\quad\quad\quad x \geq -8$

Set the radicand ≥ 0 and solve. Domain is the set of all real numbers greater than or equal to -8.

Range: Since b is 0 and a is negative, the range is the set of all real numbers less than or equal to 0.

Sketch:

x	$g(x)$
-8	0
-7	-2
-4	-4
1	-6

228

Lesson 38: Radical Functions

3. Determine the domain and range and sketch $h(x) = 5\sqrt{x-3} + 4$

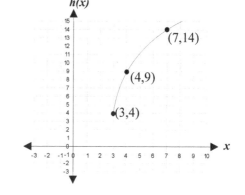

Domain: $x - 3 \geq 0$

$x \geq 3$

Set the radicand ≥ 0 and solve. Domain is the set of all real numbers greater than or equal to 3.

Range: Since a is positive, the range is the set of all real numbers greater than or equal to 4.

Sketch:

x	$h(x)$
3	4
4	9
7	14
12	19

4. Determine the domain and range and sketch $j(x) = -3\sqrt{x+4} - 5$

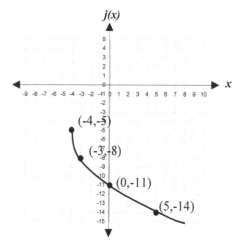

Domain: $x + 4 \geq 0$

$x \geq -4$

Set the radicand ≥ 0 and solve. Domain is the set of all real numbers greater than or equal to -4.

Range: Since a is negative, the range is the set of all real numbers less than or equal to -5.

Sketch:

x	$j(x)$
-4	-5
-3	-8
0	-11
5	-14

229

5. Determine the domain and range and sketch $k(x) = 3\sqrt{x} + 6$

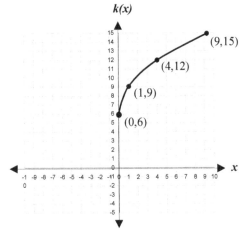

k(x)

Domain: $x \geq 0$
Domain is the set of all real numbers greater than or equal to 0.

Range: Since a is positive, the range is the set of all real numbers greater than or equal to 6.

Sketch:

x	$k(x)$
0	6
1	9
4	12
9	15

6. Determine the domain and range and sketch $l(x) = -4\sqrt{x-2} + 3$

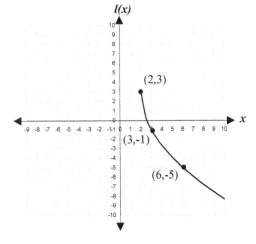

l(x)

Domain: $x - 2 \geq 0$
$x \geq 2$

Set the radicand ≥ 0 and solve. Domain is the set of all real numbers greater than or equal to 2.

Range: Since a is negative, the range is the set of all real numbers less than or equal to 3.

Sketch:

x	$l(x)$
2	3
3	-1
6	-5
11	-9

Lesson 39: Solving Radical Equations

Now let's solve some equations that contain radicals.

Example 1. $\sqrt{x} = 5$ To solve this equation, you need to remember one of our basic principles when solving an equation: whatever you do to one side of an equation, you must do the same thing to the other side. In this case, we want to square the left side so we will get rid of the radical. If we do that we must square the right side of the equation. Here is how it looks:

$$(\sqrt{x})^2 = 5^2$$
$$x = 25$$

With radical equations, just as with rational equations, you need to check the answers. It is possible to solve the equation correctly, but get an extraneous solution. Checking **Example 1**, we get:

$$\sqrt{25} = 5 \qquad \qquad \text{The answer checks so our solution, } x = 25 \text{ is valid.}$$

Example 2. $\sqrt{x} + 4 = 7$ Before we square both sides, we need to isolate the radical by using the addition property of equality.

$$\sqrt{x} + 4 = 7$$
$$\sqrt{x} = 3 \qquad \qquad \text{Subtract 4 from each side.}$$
$$(\sqrt{x})^2 = 3^2 \qquad \qquad \text{Square both sides.}$$
$$x = 9$$

Check: $\sqrt{9} + 4 = 7$ The answer checks so our solution, $x = 9$ is

$\qquad \quad 3 + 4 = 7$ valid.

Example 3. $\sqrt{3x + 7} = \sqrt{6x - 11}$ Here we have a radical on each side of the equation, so we can square each side first and then solve the resulting linear equation.

$$\sqrt{3x + 7} = \sqrt{6x - 11}$$
$$(\sqrt{3x + 7})^2 = (\sqrt{6x - 11})^2 \qquad \text{Square both sides.}$$
$$3x + 7 = 6x - 11 \qquad \text{Solve the resulting linear equation.}$$
$$18 = 3x$$
$$6 = x$$

Check the solution $x = 6$:

$$\sqrt{3(6) + 7} = \sqrt{6(6) - 11}$$
$$\sqrt{25} = \sqrt{25} \qquad \qquad \text{The answer checks so our solution } x = 6$$
$$5 = 5 \qquad \qquad \text{is valid.}$$

Example 4. $2\sqrt{x+1}+7 = x$

Isolate the radical, then square both sides and solve the resulting equation.

$2\sqrt{x+1}+7 = x$

$2\sqrt{x+1} = x-7$ Isolate the radical.

$2^2(x+1) = (x-7)^2$ Square both sides.

$4x+4 = x^2 -14x+49$

$0 = x^2 -18x+45$ Solve the quadratic equation.

$0 = (x-15)(x-3)$

$x = 15, 3$

✓ Now let's check each answer.

For $x = 15$:

$2\sqrt{x+1}+7 = x$

$2\sqrt{15+1}+7 = 15$

$2 \bullet 4 + 7 = 15$

$15 = 15$

This answer checks so
the solution $x = 15$ is
valid.

For $x = 3$:

$2\sqrt{x+1}+7 = x$

$2\sqrt{3+1}+7 = 3$

$2 \bullet 2 + 7 = 3$

$11 \neq 3$

This answer does not check so
the solution $x = 3$ is not valid.

Now it's your turn.

Lesson 39: Solving Radical Equations

Exercises

1. Solve: $\sqrt{x} = 6$

2. Solve: $\sqrt{x} = \dfrac{4}{3}$

3. Solve: $\sqrt{x} - 5 = 2$

4. Solve: $3 = \sqrt{x} - 8$

5. Solve: $\sqrt{2x+5} = \sqrt{4x-3}$

6. Solve: $\sqrt{5x-4} = \sqrt{2x+8}$

7. Solve: $\sqrt{x-3} = x-5$

8. Solve: $\sqrt{x+3} - 3 = x$

9. Solve: $\sqrt{7x+4} + 8 = x$

10. Solve: $\quad 4 + \sqrt{2x-8} = x$

11. Solve: $\quad \sqrt{3x+15} = x+5$

12. Solve: $\quad \sqrt{7x+2} = \sqrt{2x+17}$

Lesson 39: Solving Radical Equations

Solutions

1. Solve: $\sqrt{x} = 6$

   $x = 36$

   Square both sides of the equation.

   Check: $\sqrt{36} = 6$

   The answer checks so the solution $x = 36$ is valid.

2. Solve: $\sqrt{x} = \dfrac{4}{3}$

   $x = \dfrac{16}{9}$

   Square both sides of the equation.

   Check: $\sqrt{\dfrac{16}{9}} = \dfrac{4}{3}$

   The answer checks so the solution $x = \dfrac{16}{9}$ is valid.

3. Solve: $\sqrt{x} - 5 = 2$

   $\sqrt{x} = 7$

   $x = 49$

   Isolate the radical by adding 5 to each side, then square each side.

   Check: $\sqrt{49} - 5 = 2$

   $7 - 5 = 2$

   $2 = 2$

   The answer checks so the solution $x = 49$ is valid.

4. Solve: $3 = \sqrt{x} - 8$

   $11 = \sqrt{x}$

   $121 = x$

   Isolate the radical by adding 8 to each side, then square each side.

   Check: $3 = \sqrt{121} - 8$

   $3 = 11 - 3$

   $3 = 3$

   The answer checks so the solution $x = 121$ is valid.

5. Solve: $\sqrt{2x+5} = \sqrt{4x-3}$

   $2x + 5 = 4x - 3$

   $8 = 2x$

   $4 = x$

   Square each side, then solve the resulting linear equation.

   Check: $\sqrt{2(4)+5} = \sqrt{4(4)-3}$

   $\sqrt{13} = \sqrt{13}$

   The answer checks so the solution $x = 4$ is valid.

6. Solve: $\sqrt{5x-4} = \sqrt{2x+8}$

   $5x - 4 = 2x + 8$

   $3x = 12$

   $x = 4$

   Square each side, then solve the resulting linear equation.

   Check: $\sqrt{5(4)-4} = \sqrt{2(4)+8}$

   $\sqrt{16} = \sqrt{16}$

   The answer checks so the solution $x = 4$ is valid.

7. Solve: $\sqrt{x-3} = x-5$

$$x-3 = x^2 - 10x + 25$$
$$0 = x^2 - 11x + 28$$
$$0 = (x-7)(x-4)$$
$$x = 7, 4$$

Square each side, then solve the resulting quadratic equation.

Check $x = 7$: $\sqrt{7-3} = 7-5$
$$2 = 2$$

Check $x = 4$: $\sqrt{4-3} = 4-5$
$$1 \neq -1$$

The only valid solution is $x = 7$.

8. Solve: $\sqrt{x+3} - 3 = x$

$$\sqrt{x+3} = x+3$$
$$x+3 = x^2 + 6x + 9$$
$$0 = x^2 + 5x + 6$$
$$0 = (x+2)(x+3)$$
$$x = -2, -3$$

Isolate the radical by adding 3 to each side. Square each side, then solve the resulting quadratic equation.

Check $x = -2$: $\sqrt{-2+3} - 3 = -2$
$$\sqrt{1} - 3 = -2$$
$$-2 = -2$$

Check $x = -3$: $\sqrt{-3+3} - 3 = -3$
$$-3 = -3$$

Both solutions check, so there are two valid solutions: $x = -2$, and -3.

9. Solve: $\sqrt{7x+4}+8=x$

$$\sqrt{7x+4}=x-8$$
$$7x+4=x^2-16x+64$$
$$0=x^2-23x+60$$
$$0=(x-20)(x-3)$$
$$x=20,3$$

Isolate the radical by subtracting 8 from each side. Square each side, then solve the resulting quadratic equation.

Check $x=20$: $\quad\sqrt{7(20)+4}+8=20$
$$\sqrt{144}+8=20$$
$$12+8=20$$
$$20=20$$

Check $x=3$: $\quad\sqrt{7(3)+4}+8=3$
$$\sqrt{25}+8=3$$
$$13\neq3$$

The only valid solution is $x=20$.

10. Solve: $4+\sqrt{2x-8}=x$

$$\sqrt{2x-8}=x-4$$
$$2x-8=x^2-8x+16$$
$$0=x^2-10x+24$$
$$0=(x-6)(x-4)$$
$$x=6,4$$

Isolate the radical by subtracting 4 from each side. Square each side, then solve the resulting quadratic equation.

Check $x=6$: $\quad4+\sqrt{2(6)-8}=6$
$$4+\sqrt{4}=6$$
$$6=6$$

Check $x=4$: $\quad4+\sqrt{2(4)-8}=4$
$$4+\sqrt{0}=4$$
$$4=4$$

Both solutions check, so there are two valid solutions: $x=6$ and 4.

11. Solve: $\sqrt{3x+15} = x+5$

$$3x+15 = x^2 +10x+25$$

$$0 = x^2 +7x+10$$

$$0 = (x+5)(x+2)$$

$$x = -5, -2$$

Square each side, then solve the resulting quadratic equation.

Check $x = -5$: $\sqrt{3(-5)+15} = -5+5$

$$0 = 0$$

Check $x = -2$: $\sqrt{3(-2)+15} = -2+5$

$$\sqrt{9} = 3$$

$$3 = 3$$

Both solutions check, so there are two valid solutions: $x = -5$ and -2.

12. Solve: $\sqrt{7x+2} = \sqrt{2x+17}$

$$7x+2 = 2x+17$$

$$5x = 15$$

$$x = 3$$

Square both sides, then solve the resulting linear equation.

Check $x = 3$: $\sqrt{7(3)+2} = \sqrt{2(3)+17}$

$$\sqrt{23} = \sqrt{23}$$

The answer checks so the solution $x = 3$ is valid.

40 – Intermediate Algebra Practice Test

1. Let $f(x) = 4x - 7$ and $g(x) = -2x + 5$

    a. Find $f(-2) + g(3)$ Answer:_____

    b. Find $f(a) + g(a)$ Answer:_____

    c. For what value of x is $f(x) = 9$ Answer:_____

2. In 1980, Company ABC sold 400 surfboards; in 1995, they sold 625 surfboards. Let $f(t)$ represent the number of surfboards sold t years after 1980. Assume $f(t)$ is a linear function.

    a. Write an equation for $f(t)$ expressing the number   Answer:_____
    of surfboards sold in terms of t.

    b. Predict the number of surfboards sold in the year 2003.   Answer:_____

    c. Determine when the company will sell 820 surfboards.   Answer:_____

3. Simplify:

    a. $81^{\frac{3}{4}}$ Answer:_____

    b. $6^{\frac{2}{3}} \bullet 6^{\frac{4}{3}}$ Answer:_____

    c. $x^{\frac{4}{5}} \bullet x^{\frac{1}{3}}$ Answer:_____

    d. $\dfrac{a^{\frac{2}{5}}}{a^{\frac{1}{4}}}$ Answer:_____

    e. $36^{-\frac{1}{2}}$ Answer:_____

    f. $\dfrac{a^2 b^{-5} c^3}{(2a^{-1}bc^2)^{-3}}$ Answer:_____

4. a. Complete the table of values for the functions shown:

$$f(x) = 4^x \qquad\qquad g(x) = -2\left(\frac{1}{3}\right)^x$$

x	$f(x)$	$g(x)$
-2		
-1		
0		
1		
2		

b. Graph $f(x)$

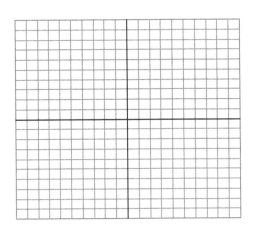

5. Solve:

   a. $5x^3 = 40$ Answer:_____

   b. $2x^2 - 2 = 48$ Answer:_____

   c. $6x^3 = 60$ Answer:_____

6. Find the inverse of $f(x) = -2x + 5$ Answer:_____

7. Write $2^4 = 16$ as a logarithmic equation.   Answer:_____

8. Write $\log_5 125 = 3$ as an exponential equation.

Answer:_____

9. Solve the following equations for x:

    a. $\log_4 x = 3$

    Answer:_____

    b. $\log x = 2$

    Answer:_____

    c. $\ln e = x$

    Answer:_____

    d. $5^x = 17$

    Answer:_____

    e. $3(2^x) = 42$

    Answer:_____

10. Given: $y = x^2 - 4x - 21$
    a. Find the x intercept(s):

    Answer:_____

    b. Find the y intercept:

    Answer:_____

    c. Find the coordinates of the vertex:

    Answer:_____

    d. Graph the function:

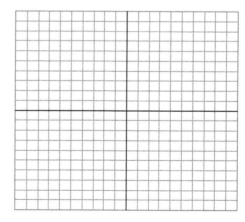

11. Solve, and write the answer as a complex number
in simplest form: $3x^2 + 10x + 12 = 0$

Answer:_____

12. Solve the system of equations:
$$y = x^2 - 7$$
$$3x - y = 9$$

Answer:_____

13. Simplify and find the domain of:
$$f(x) = \frac{2x - 8}{x^2 + x - 20}$$

Answer:_____

14. Find the domain and range for:

$$f(x) = -3\sqrt{x - 2} + 4$$

Answer:_____

40 – Intermediate Algebra Practice Test

Answers to Intermediate Algebra Practice Test

1. Let $f(x) = 4x - 7$ and $g(x) = -2x + 5$

    a. Find $f(-2) + g(3)$ Answer: -16

    b. Find $f(a) + g(a)$ Answer: $2a - 2$

    c. For what value of x is $f(x) = 9$ Answer: $x = 4$

See Lesson 46 for explanations.

2. In 1980, Company ABC sold 400 surfboards; in 1995, they sold 625 surfboards. Let $f(t)$ represent the number of surfboards sold t years after 1980. Assume $f(t)$ is a linear function.

    a. Write an equation for $f(t)$ expressing the number   Answer: $f(t) = 15t + 400$
of surfboards sold in terms of t.

    b. Predict the number of surfboards sold in the year 2003.   Answer: 745

    c. Determine when the company will sell 820 surfboards.   Answer: Year 2008

See Lesson 47 for explanations.

3. Simplify:

    a. $81^{\frac{3}{4}}$ Answer: 27

    b. $6^{\frac{2}{3}} \bullet 6^{\frac{4}{3}}$ Answer: 36

    c. $x^{\frac{4}{5}} \bullet x^{\frac{1}{3}}$ Answer: $x^{\frac{17}{15}}$

    d. $\dfrac{a^{\frac{2}{5}}}{a^{\frac{1}{4}}}$ Answer: $a^{\frac{3}{20}}$

    e. $36^{-\frac{1}{2}}$ Answer: $\dfrac{1}{6}$

    f. $\dfrac{a^2 b^{-5} c^3}{(2a^{-1}bc^2)^{-3}}$ Answer: $\dfrac{8c^9}{ab^2}$

See Lesson 48 for explanations.

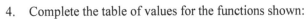
4. Complete the table of values for the functions shown:

$f(x) = 4^x$ $\qquad\qquad g(x) = -2\left(\dfrac{1}{3}\right)^x$

x	$f(x)$	$g(x)$
-2	$\dfrac{1}{16}$	-18
-1	$\dfrac{1}{4}$	-6
0	1	-2
1	4	$-\dfrac{2}{3}$
2	16	$-\dfrac{2}{9}$

Graph $f(x)$

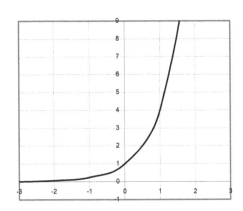

See Lesson 49 for explanations.

5. Solve:

a. $5x^3 = 40$ $\qquad$ Answer: $\underline{x = 2}$

b. $2x^2 - 2 = 48$ $\qquad$ Answer: $\underline{x = \pm 5}$

c. $6x^3 = 60$ $\qquad$ Answer: $\underline{x = 10^{\frac{1}{3}}}$

See lesson 51 for explanations.

6. Find the inverse of $f(x) = -2x + 5$ $\qquad$ Answer: $\underline{f^{-1}(x) = -\dfrac{1}{2}x + \dfrac{5}{2}}$

See lesson 52 for explanations.

7. Write $2^4 = 16$ as a logarithmic equation. $\qquad$ Answer: $\underline{\log_2 16 = 4}$

See lesson 52 for explanations.

8. Write $\log_5 125 = 3$ as an exponential equation.

    Answer: $5^3 = 125$

    See lesson 52 for explanations.

9. Solve the following equations for x:

    a. $\log_4 x = 3$

    Answer: $x = 64$

    b. $\log x = 2$

    Answer: $x = 100$

    c. $\ln e = x$

    Answer: $x = 1$

    d. $5^x = 17$

    Answer: $x = \dfrac{\log 17}{\log 5}$

    e. $3(2^x) = 42$

    Answer: $x = \dfrac{\log 14}{\log 2}$

    See lessons 53, 54, and 55 for explanations.

10. Given: $y = x^2 - 4x - 21$

    a. Find the x intercept(s):

    Answer: $(7, 0)$ and $(-3, 0)$

    b. Find the y intercept:

    Answer: $(0, -21)$

    c. Find the coordinates of the vertex:

    Answer: $(2, -25)$

    d. Graph the function:

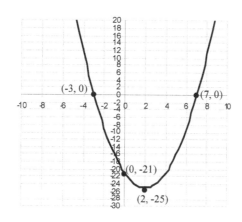

    See lesson 56 for explanations.

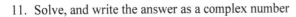

11. Solve, and write the answer as a complex number

    in simplest form: $3x^2 + 10x + 12 = 0$ Answer: $-\dfrac{5}{3} \pm \dfrac{\sqrt{11}}{3} i$

    See lesson 57 for explanations.

12. Solve the system of equations:

    $y = x^2 - 7$

    $3x - y = 9$ Answer: $(1, -6)$ and $(2, -3)$

    See lesson 58 for explanations.

13. Simplify and find the domain for:

    $f(x) = \dfrac{2x - 8}{x^2 + x - 20}$ Simplified: $f(x) = \dfrac{2}{x + 5}$

    Domain: Set of all real numbers except $x = 4, -5$

    See lesson 59 for explanations.

14. Find the domain and range for:

    $f(x) = -3\sqrt{x - 2} + 4$ Domain: Set of all real numbers ≥ 2

    Range: Set of all real numbers ≤ 4

    See lesson 61 for explanations.

Extra Problem Sets

Elementary Algebra

Extra Problem Set: Working with Formulas

1. $I = Prt$ Solve for r

2. $y = mx + b$ Solve for m

3. $h = \dfrac{v^2}{2g}$ Solve for v^2

4. $A = \pi r^2$ Solve for π

5. $P = 2l + 2w$ Solve for w

6. $M = \dfrac{1}{5}n$ Solve for n

7. $E = IR$ Solve for I

8. $E = mc^2$ Solve for m

9. $Ax + By = C$ Solve for x

10. $A = \dfrac{1}{2}bh$ Solve for b

11. $d = rt$ Solve for t

12. $A = \dfrac{a+b}{2}$ Solve for b

13. $P = \dfrac{-2t}{s}$ Solve for t

14. $Q = 3x + 2y$ Solve for y

15. $F = \dfrac{9}{5}C + 32$ Solve for C

16. $W = \dfrac{Lg^2}{800}$ solve for L

17. $y = 5x + 3$ Solve for x

18. $2x + 3y = 12$ Solve for y

19. $Z = \dfrac{5}{m+n}$ Solve for m

20. $6x - 3y = 24$ Solve for y

Extra Problem Set: Solving Inequalities

Solve.

1. $8 + 4x < 32$

2. $29 \geq 8 + 7x$

3. $-7x + 8 < -41$

4. $3(7 + 2x) \geq 30 + 7(x - 1)$

5. Solve and graph: $3x < -x + 8$

6. Solve and graph: $4y + 13 > -11 - 2y$

7. Solve and graph: $x + 12 \leq 5x$

8. Solve and graph: $-6x - 6 \geq 2x + 18$

9. $19 - 7a > 3a + 39$

10. $9 - 7x < 5 - 6x + 2$

11. $-4 < 9y + 6 - 7y$

12. $4b + 2 \leq 3b + 9$

13. $23 - 7z \geq 11z - 13$

14. $-18y \geq -2 - 16y$

15. $4(2x - 3) < 28$

16. $16a + 4 < 28a + 28$

17. $3(2x - 3) \leq 27$

18. $\dfrac{x}{4} - 3 > 2$

19. $\dfrac{x}{3} + 2 < \dfrac{2}{3}$

20. $7x - 6 > 6x - 8$

Extra Problem Set: Graphing

1. $4x + 3y = -12$ Graph by plotting the intercepts.
2. $-4x + 6y = 24$ Graph by plotting the intercepts.

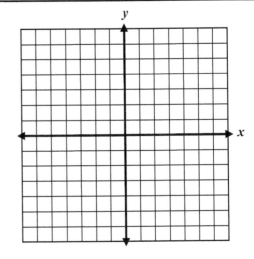

3. Determine the slope and y intercept of: a) $y = 3x + 6$

   b) $y = -2x - 7$

4. Determine the slope and y intercept of: a) $4x + 2y = -16$

   b) $3x + 4y = 7$

5. Determine the slope of the line through these two points: a) (-2,3) and (3,-4)

   b) (-1,-5) and (-6,-7)

6. Determine the slope of the line through these two points: a) (-1,-2) and (-4,-5)

   b) (4,-3) and (2,-5)

7. Find the equation of the line with a slope of 5 passing through the point: (3, 4)

8. Find the equation of the line with a slope of –2 passing through the point: (5, -3)

9. Find the equation of the line that contains these two points: (1, 1) and (-2, 10)

10. Determine if these lines are parallel, perpendicular, or neither: $3x + 6y = 5$

   $4y = -2x - 5$

Extra Problem Set: Rules for Exponents

1. $x^3 x^5$

2. $(x^3)^5$

3. $\dfrac{y^7}{y^4}$

4. $\dfrac{a^6 b^2 c}{a^{-3} b^3 c^2}$

5. $\left(\dfrac{x^{-5} y^{-3}}{x^3 y^4}\right)^2$

6. $(-2x^3)^4$

7. $(-5x^2 y)(-2x^5 y^4)$

8. $(-3x^{-3} y^{-4} z^2)^2 (4x^{-1} y^2 z^3)$

9. 5^{-3}

10. $\dfrac{1}{5^{-3}}$

11. $\dfrac{y^{-3}}{y^{-4}}$

12. $\dfrac{x^2 y^{-3}}{x^{-5} y^2}$

13. $-3x^2$

14. $(-3x)^2$

15. $\dfrac{-2x^3 y}{-6x^{-4} y}$

16. $(2ab^3)(-3a^{-2} b^{-3})$

17. $-3(xyz^2)(x^2 y^2 z)^2$

18. $\dfrac{1}{x^{-3} y}$

19. Evaluate: $y^0 - \dfrac{1}{y^{-2}} + 10y$ for $y = 3$

20. Evaluate: $x^0 + x^{-1} + 18x^{-2}$ for $x = -3$

Extra Problem Set: Scientific Notation

1. Convert 275,000 to scientific notation

2. Convert 0.00000724 to scientific notation

3. Convert 4.286×10^5 from scientific notation to decimal notation

4. Convert 7.67×10^{-6} from scientific notation to decimal notation

5. Multiply: a) $(2.24 \times 10^3)(3.6 \times 10^2)$ b) $(4.24 \times 10^4)(1.75 \times 10^3)$

6. Multiply: a) $(8.26 \times 10^{-2})(6.1 \times 10^7)$ b) $(9.25 \times 10^3)(2.414 \times 10^{-6})$

7. Multiply: a) $(5.25 \times 10^{-3})(3.5 \times 10^{-5})$ b) $(2.48 \times 10^{-2})(4.82 \times 10^{-7})$

8. Divide: a) $(4.2 \times 10^3) \div (8.4 \times 10^5)$ b) $(1.44 \times 10^4) \div (3.6 \times 10^5)$

9. Divide: a) $\dfrac{(2.1 \times 10^6)}{(5.25 \times 10^{-3})}$ b) $\dfrac{(4.2 \times 10^6)}{(1.12 \times 10^3)}$

10. Divide: a) $\dfrac{(1.6 \times 10^{-5})}{(6.4 \times 10^{-8})}$ b) $\dfrac{(1.12 \times 10^{-5})}{(5.6 \times 10^3)}$

Extra Problem Set: Special Products of Binomials

1. $(x-4)(x+4)$

2. $(3y+6)(3y-6)$

3. $(5z-1)(5z+1)$

4. $(7a+5b)(7a-5b)$

5. $(x+8)^2$

6. $(3y+4)^2$

7. $(7z+3)^2$

8. $(x-11)^2$

9. $(6y-7)^2$

10. $(9a-4b)^2$

11. $(x+9)(x-9)$

12. $(4-2y)(4+2y)$

13. $(s+t)(s-t)$

14. $(3c-5d)(3c+5d)$

15. $(y+12)^2$

16. $(4x+2y)^2$

17. $(3a+8b)^2$

18. $(15-2x)^2$

19. $(y-x)^2$

20. $(40-2x)^2$

Extra Problem Set: Introduction to Factoring

Factor the following.

1. $5x + 20$

2. $2y^2 + 14y$

3. $4y^2 + 12y$

4. $9z^3 - 36z^2 - 18z$

5. $x^2 + 8x + 15$

6. $z^2 - 12z + 32$

7. $a^2 - 11a + 28$

8. $y^2 + y - 72$

9. $2x^2 - 10x - 72$

10. $3y^2 - 21y - 180$

11. $a^2 - 11a + 10$

12. $y^2 + 21y - 72$

13. $15x^2 + 3x$

14. $40 - 3x - x^2$

15. $x^2 + 8xy + 15y^2$

16. $y^4 - 11y^2 + 24$

17. $x^2 - 7x - 18$

18. $x^2 + 28x + 96$

19. $2x^2 + 4x - 30$

20. $x^2 + x + 1$

Extra Problem Set: Factoring Squares

Factor the following.

1. $y^2 - 81$

2. $9a^2 - 64b^2$

3. $9x^2 + 25$

4. $x^2 + 16x + 64$

5. $2y^2 - 32y + 128$

6. $4a^2 + 28ab + 49b^2$

7. $x^4 + 10x^2 + 25$

8. $a^4 - 64$

9. $100x^4 - 9$

10. $25x^4 - 1$

11. $16b^2 - 25c^2$

12. $4x^2 - 8x + 4$

13. $x^2 - 6xy + 9y^2$

14. $8c^2 - 98$

15. $x^4 - 1$

16. $16x^2 - 40x + 25$

17. $49x^2 - 81y^2$

18. $x^3 - 24x^2 + 144x$

19. $49 - 42x + 9x^2$

20. $25x^2 + 36y^2$

Extra Problem Set: Factoring Using Grouping

Factor the following.

1. $y^2(y+3) - 2(y+3)$

2. $6x^3 + 3x^2 + 2x + 1$

3. $10x^3 - 25x^2 + 4x - 10$

4. $5a^3 - 5a^2 + a - 1$

5. $5x^2 - x - 18$

6. $3x^2 + 4x + 1$

7. $9x^2 + 6x - 8$

8. $18x^2 + 3x - 10$

9. $72x^3 + 120x^2 + 50x$

10. $49 - 42x + 9x^2$

11. $x^2(x-6) + 4(x-6)$

12. $18y^3 - 21y^2 + 30y - 35$

13. $4x^2 - 25x + 21$

14. $6y^2 + 13y - 8$

15. $9x^2 + 24xy + 16y^2$

16. $3x^2 + 4x - 15$

17. $15y^2 - 19y - 10$

18. $6y^2 - 13y + 6$

19. $12a^2 - 17a - 5$

20. $30x^2 - 69x + 36$

Extra Problem Set: Solving Quadratic Equations by Factoring

1. $6x(x-5)=0$

2. $(y+2)(y+7)=0$

3. $z^2-2z-35=0$

4. $a^2+12a+27=0$

5. $4x^2-121=0$

6. $4x^2-28x+49=0$

7. $3x^2=5+2x$

8. $25y^2=81$

9. $x^2+6x+2=-x-4$

10. $0=64+x^2+16x$

11. $3y(y+8)=0$

12. $(x+4)(x-3)=0$

13. $(2x+1)(3x-4)=0$

14. $x^2-3x-18=0$

15. $9y^2-100=0$

16. $6x^2+11x+4=0$

17. $3x^2+x-2=0$

18. $x^2=-2x-1$

19. $2x^2+5x+2=0$

20. $x^2-4x+4=0$

Extra Problem Set: Rational Expressions - Multiplication

Multiply and simplify.

1. $\dfrac{2}{5} \bullet \dfrac{x}{y}$

2. $\dfrac{5x}{3y} \bullet \dfrac{x+2}{2y}$

3. $\dfrac{2x}{5} \bullet \dfrac{15}{4x^4}$

4. $\dfrac{2a^3}{3a+15} \bullet \dfrac{a+5}{a}$

5. $\dfrac{a^2-36}{4a} \bullet \dfrac{6a^2}{a+6}$

6. $\dfrac{3x+6}{x^2-6x-16} \bullet \dfrac{x^2+7x+12}{2x+6}$

7. $\dfrac{y^2-36}{6y^2-24} \bullet \dfrac{8y+16}{y-6}$

8. $\dfrac{x^2-10x+21}{x^2-49} \bullet \dfrac{x+3}{x^2-9}$

9. $\dfrac{x^2-6x-7}{x^2-1} \bullet \dfrac{x-1}{x-7}$

10. $\dfrac{x^2-7x+10}{x^2-4} \bullet \dfrac{x+4}{x-5}$

11. $\dfrac{4x^2}{3x^2-12x+12} \bullet \dfrac{3x-6}{x}$

12. $\dfrac{y^2-9}{y} \bullet \dfrac{y^2-3y}{y^2+y-12}$

13. $\dfrac{x^4-16}{x^4-1} \bullet \dfrac{x^2+1}{x^2+4}$

14. $\dfrac{4y+32}{y^2-y-6} \bullet \dfrac{6y+12}{y^2+9y+8}$

15. $\dfrac{x^2-1}{x-1} \bullet \dfrac{x^2-1}{x+1}$

16. $\dfrac{a^2-25}{a^2+5a+6} \bullet \dfrac{a^2-9}{a^2+a-20}$

17. $\dfrac{18}{x^4} \bullet \dfrac{5x}{4}$

18. $\dfrac{4xy^2}{3y} \bullet \dfrac{6x}{xy^3}$

19. $\dfrac{y^2+10y-11}{y^2-1} \bullet \dfrac{y+1}{y+11}$

20. $\dfrac{x+5}{y-4} \bullet \dfrac{y+4}{x-5}$

258

Extra Problem Set: Rational Expressions – Division

1. Find the reciprocal of: a) $\dfrac{3x-5}{x+2}$ b) $\dfrac{2y-9}{y-7}$

2. Divide and simplify: a) $\dfrac{4x}{y} \div \dfrac{15y}{2}$ b) $\dfrac{6a}{7b} \div \dfrac{2b}{3a}$

3. Divide and simplify: a) $\dfrac{3y}{4x} \div \dfrac{9y^2}{8}$ b) $\dfrac{4x}{5y} \div \dfrac{8x^2}{10y^2}$

4. Divide and simplify: a) $\dfrac{6a^2}{5b} \div \dfrac{18a}{5b^2}$ b) $\dfrac{15x^2}{8y} \div \dfrac{10x}{4y^2}$

5. Divide and simplify: $\dfrac{4a^2-49}{a^2} \div \dfrac{2a-7}{a^3}$

6. Divide and simplify: $\dfrac{x^2+x-12}{15} \div \dfrac{x-3}{5x+10}$

7. Divide and simplify: $\dfrac{3y-12}{y^2+3y-4} \div \dfrac{3}{y-1}$

8. Divide and simplify: $\dfrac{x^2+8x+15}{x^2+9x+20} \div \dfrac{x+3}{x+5}$

9. Divide and simplify: $\dfrac{x^2-49}{x^2+4x-32} \div \dfrac{3x}{x^2+9x+8}$

10. Divide and simplify: $\dfrac{4x^4-4}{4x+4} \div \dfrac{x^2+1}{4}$

11. Divide and simplify: $\dfrac{y-3}{12} \div \dfrac{4y-12}{9}$

12. Divide and simplify: $\dfrac{a^2+3a}{a^2+2a-3} \div \dfrac{a}{a+1}$

Extra Problem Set: Rational Expressions – Add & Subtract

Simplify.

1. $\dfrac{7x}{x+4}+\dfrac{3x}{x+4}$

2. $\dfrac{10y}{y-3}+\dfrac{3y}{y-3}$

3. $\dfrac{7}{x}+\dfrac{5x}{3x^2}$

4. $\dfrac{8}{3x^2}+\dfrac{5x}{4x}$

5. $\dfrac{3y^2}{y+1}-\dfrac{4}{y+1}$

6. $\dfrac{2x}{3x-5}-\dfrac{5}{3x-5}$

7. $\dfrac{3y}{y^2}-\dfrac{7}{3y^3}$

8. $\dfrac{5}{3a}-\dfrac{7}{4a^2}$

9. $\dfrac{2x}{3x-2}-\dfrac{3x}{x+1}$

10. $\dfrac{2a}{a^2-16}+\dfrac{a}{a-4}$

11. $\dfrac{y}{2y}-\dfrac{4}{3y^2}$

12. $\dfrac{x}{x^2+5x+4}+\dfrac{4}{x^2+4x+3}$

13. $\dfrac{10}{x^2-x-6}-\dfrac{2x}{x^2+4x+4}$

14. $\dfrac{3}{x^2-5x+6}+\dfrac{x}{x^2+2x-8}$

15. $\dfrac{a+b}{ab^2}+\dfrac{2a+b}{a^2b^2}$

16. $\dfrac{4}{x+2}-\dfrac{3}{x-2}$

17. $\dfrac{4x}{x^2-16}-\dfrac{x}{x+4}$

18. $\dfrac{x+2}{x-7}+\dfrac{x-3}{x^2-49}$

19. $\dfrac{3}{(x-1)^2}-\dfrac{4}{x-1}$

20. $\dfrac{5}{t+4}+\dfrac{6}{3t+12}$

Extra Problem Set: Systems of Equations - Graphing

1. Is the given ordered pair a solution for the system of equations?

    a) (2,4)
    $$3x - 2y = -2$$
    $$x + 2y = 8$$

    b) (-1,-5)
    $$4x + y = -9$$
    $$6x = 4 + 2y$$

    c) (3,2)
    $$2x + 3y = 12$$
    $$x = 4y - 5$$

2. Solve this system of equations by graphing:

    (1) $y = x + 1$
    (2) $y = -2x + 10$

    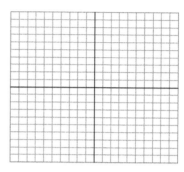

3. Solve this system of equations by graphing:
    (1) $y = 2x + 1$
    (2) $3x + y = -9$

    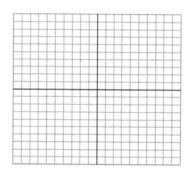

4. Solve this system of equations by graphing:
    (1) $y = 2x - 7$
    (2) $x + y = 2$

    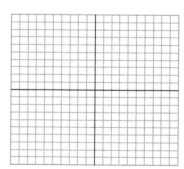

5. Solve this system of equations by graphing:
    (1) $x = -3$
    (2) $y = 2$

    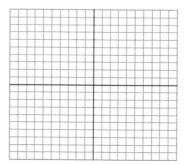

Extra Problem Set: Systems of Equations – The Substitution Method

1.   Solve by substitution: (1) $2x - 3y = 6$
    (2) $x - y = 1$

2.   Solve by substitution: (1) $x + y = -5$
    (2) $x = y + 9$

3.   Solve by substitution: (1) $2x + y = 12$
    (2) $3x - y = 13$

4.   Solve by substitution: (1) $-x + 5y = 11$
    (2) $x - 2y = -2$

5.   Solve by substitution: (1) $3x - y = 0$
    (2) $2x + 3y = 11$

6.   Solve by substitution: (1) $y - 2x = 3$
    (2) $y + 2x = -1$

7.   Solve by substitution: (1) $3x - 2y = 8$
    (2) $3y = x - 8$

Extra Problem Set: Systems of Equations – The Elimination Method

1.   Solve by elimination: (1) $4x + 5y = 0$

                                                        (2) $2x + 3y = -2$

2.   Solve by elimination: (1) $x + 4y = 6$

                                                        (2) $-x + 3y = 8$

3.   Solve by elimination: (1) $-x + 5y = 12$

                                                        (2) $-3x + 4y = 3$

4.   Solve by elimination: (1) $5x - 3y = 18$

                                                        (2) $4x - 6y = 0$

5.   Solve by elimination: (1) $x = 3y - 4$

                                                        (2) $3x + 2y = 10$

6.   Solve by elimination: (1) $3x - 4y = 5$

                                                        (2) $4x + 3y = -9$

7.   Solve by elimination: (1) $5x - 2y = 12$

                                                        (2) $4x + 3y = 5$

Extra Problem Set: Radicals

1. Find: $\sqrt{144}$

2. Find: $\sqrt{121}$

3. Multiply: $\sqrt{6}\sqrt{8}$

4. Multiply: $\sqrt{5}\sqrt{11}$

5. Multiply: $\sqrt{3}\sqrt{14}$

6. Multiply: $\sqrt{6}\sqrt{12}$

7. Simplify: $\sqrt{175}$

8. Simplify: $\sqrt{68}$

9. Simplify: $\sqrt{27}$

10. Simplify: $\sqrt{99}$

11. Simplify: $\dfrac{\sqrt{48}}{\sqrt{3}}$

12. Simplify: $\dfrac{\sqrt{30}}{\sqrt{5}}$

13. Simplify: $\sqrt{\dfrac{54}{36}}$

14. Simplify: $\sqrt{\dfrac{16}{49}}$

15. Add: $2\sqrt{5}+8\sqrt{5}$

16. Add: $4\sqrt{11}+7\sqrt{11}$

17. Subtract: $19\sqrt{3}-7\sqrt{3}$

18. Subtract: $12\sqrt{7}-4\sqrt{7}$

19. Add: $\sqrt{54}+\sqrt{96}$

20. Add: $2\sqrt{32}+6\sqrt{18}$

Extra Problem Set: The Pythagorean Theorem

Find the length of the side not given. Find the exact answer and an approximate answer to two decimal places:

1. $a = 6, b = 8$

2. $a = 10, c = 16$

3. $b = 5, c = 11$

4. $a = 3, b = 5$

5. $a = 4, c = 10$

6. $b = 2, c = 12$

7. $a = 5, b = 9$

8. $a = 3, c = 8$

9. $b = 4, c = 9$

10. $a = 7, b = 8$

Extra Problem Set: The Quadratic Formula

1. $3x^2 - 7x + 4 = 0$

2. $4x^2 + 12x - 7 = 0$

3. $y^2 - 4y - 3 = 0$

4. $(x+4)(x-1) = 8$

5. $2x^2 - 5x - 12 = -5x$

6. $x^2 - 3x - 10 = 0$

7. $x^2 + 4x - 7 = 0$

8. $3x^2 = 4x + 2$

9. $4x^2 - 5 = -4x$

10. $2x^2 - 2x = 1$

Extra Problem Set: More Word Problems

1. The hypotenuse of a right triangle is 9 inches long. One leg is 2 inches longer than the other. Find the length of each leg. Round numbers to the nearest tenth.

2. Suppose 630 tickets are sold for a Montgomery College football game for total revenue of $4125. If regular tickets cost $7.50 and student tickets cost $4.50, how many of each kind of tickets were sold?

3. The length of a rectangular garden is 3 meters greater than the width. The area of the rectangle is 108 square meters. Find the length and width of the rectangle.

4. The cost of 2 slices of pizza and 3 sodas is $8.50. The cost of 4 slices of pizza and 5 sodas is $15.50. What is the cost of one slice of pizza and what is the cost of one soda?

5. An 18 foot ladder is leaned against a building. The bottom of the ladder is 4 feet from the building. How high up the building will the ladder reach? Round to the nearest tenth of a foot.

Extra Problem Set Answers: Elementary Algebra

Working with Formulas

1) $r = \dfrac{I}{Pt}$

2) $m = \dfrac{y-b}{x}$

3) $v^2 = 2gh$

4) $\pi = \dfrac{A}{r^2}$

5) $w = \dfrac{P-2l}{2}$

6) $n = 5M$

7) $I = \dfrac{E}{R}$

8) $m = \dfrac{E}{c^2}$

9) $x = \dfrac{C-By}{A}$

10) $b = \dfrac{2A}{h}$

11) $t = \dfrac{d}{r}$

12) $b = 2A - a$

13) $t = \dfrac{Ps}{-2}$

14) $y = \dfrac{Q-3x}{2}$

15) $C = \dfrac{5F-160}{9}$

16) $L = \dfrac{800W}{g^2}$

17) $x = \dfrac{y-3}{5}$

18) $y = \dfrac{-2x+12}{3}$

19) $m = \dfrac{5-Zn}{Z}$

20) $y = 2x - 8$

Solving Inequalities

1) $x < 6$

2) $x \le 3$

3) $x > 7$

4) $x \le -2$

9) $a < -2$

10) $x > 2$

11) $y > -5$

12) $b \le 7$

13) $z \le 2$

14) $y \le 1$

15) $x < 5$

16) $a > -2$

17) $x \le 6$

18) $x > 20$

19) $x < -4$

20) $x > -2$

5) Solve and graph: $x < 2$

6) Solve and graph: $y > -4$

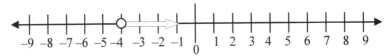

7) Solve and graph: $x \ge 3$

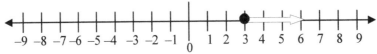

8) Solve and graph: $x \le -3$

Graphing
1) and 2)

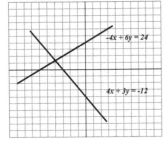

3a) $m = 3$; y-int $(0,6)$

3b) $m = -2$; y-int $(0,-7)$

4a) $m = -2$; y-int $(0,-8)$

4b) $m = -\dfrac{3}{4}$; y-int $(0,\dfrac{7}{4})$

5a) $m = -\dfrac{7}{5}$

5b) $m = \dfrac{2}{5}$

6a) $m = 1$

6b) $m = 1$

7) $y = 5x - 11$

8) $y = -2x + 7$

9) $y = -\dfrac{1}{6}x - \dfrac{7}{3}$

10) Lines are parallel

Extra Problem Set Answers: Elementary Algebra

Rules for Exponents

1) x^8

2) x^{15}

3) y^3

4) $\dfrac{a^9}{bc}$

5) $\dfrac{1}{x^{16}y^{14}}$

6) $16x^{12}$

7) $10x^7y^5$

8) $\dfrac{36z^7}{x^7y^6}$

9) $\dfrac{1}{125}$

10) 125

11) y

12) $\dfrac{x^7}{y^5}$

13) $-3x^2$

14) $9x^2$

15) $\dfrac{x^7}{3}$

16) $\dfrac{-6}{a}$

17) $-3x^5y^5z^4$

18) $\dfrac{x^3}{y}$

19) 22

20) $2\dfrac{2}{3}$

Scientific Notation

1) 2.75×10^5

2) 7.24×10^{-6}

3) $428,600$

4) $.00000767$

5a) 8.064×10^5

5b) 7.42×10^7

6a) 5.0386×10^6

6b) 2.23295×10^{-2}

7a) 1.8375×10^{-7}

7b) 1.19536×10^{-8}

8a) 5.0×10^{-3}

8b) 4.0×10^{-2}

9a) 4.0×10^8

9b) 3.75×10^3

10a) 2.5×10^2

10b) 2.0×10^{-9}

Special Products of Binomials

1) x^2-16

2) $9y^2-36$

3) $25z^2-1$

4) $49a^2-25b^2$

5) $x^2+16x+64$

6) $9y^2+24y+16$

7) $49z^2+42z+9$

8) $x^2-22x+121$

9) $36y^2-84y+49$

10) $81a^2-72ab+16b^2$

11) x^2-81

12) $16-4y^2$

13) s^2-t^2

14) $9c^2-25d^2$

15) $y^2+24y+144$

16) $16x^2+16xy+4y^2$

17) $9a^2+48ab+64b^2$

18) $225-60x+4x^2$

19) $y^2-2xy+x^2$

20) $1600-160x+4x^2$

Introduction to Factoring

1) $5(x+4)$

2) $2y(y+7)$

3) $4y(y+3)$

4) $9z(z^2-4z-2)$

5) $(x+5)(x+3)$

6) $(z-8)(z-4)$

7) $(a-7)(a-4)$

8) $(y+9)(y-8)$

9) $2(x-9)(x+4)$

10) $3(y-12)(y+5)$

11) $(a-10)(a-1)$

12) $(y+24)(y-3)$

13) $3x(5x+1)$

14) $(8+x)(5-x)$

15) $(x+3y)(x+5y)$

16) $(y^2-8)(y^2-3)$

17) $(x-9)(x+2)$

18) $(x+4)(x+24)$

19) $2(x+5)(x-3)$

20) Can't be factored.

Factoring Squares

1) $(y-9)(y+9)$

2) $(3a-8b)(3a+8b)$

3) Can't be factored.

4) $(x+8)^2$

5) $2(y-8)^2$

6) $(2a+7b)^2$

7) $(x^2+5)^2$

8) $(a^2-8)(a^2+8)$

9) $(10x^2-3)(10x^2+3)$

10) $(5x^2-1)(5x^2+1)$

11) $(4b+5c)(4b-5c)$

12) $4(x-1)^2$

13) $(x-3y)^2$

14) $2(2c-7)(2c+7)$

15) $(x-1)(x+1)(x^2+1)$

16) $(4x-5)^2$

17) $(7x-9y)(7x+9y)$

18) $x(x-12)^2$

19) $(7-3x)^2$

20) Can't be factored.

Factoring Using Grouping

1) $(y^2-2)(y+3)$

2) $(3x^2+1)(2x+1)$

3) $(5x^2+2)(2x-5)$

4) $(5a^2+1)(a-1)$

5) $(5x+9)(x-2)$

6) $(3x+1)(x+1)$

7) $(3x-2)(3x+4)$

8) $(3x-2)(6x+5)$

9) $2x(6x+5)^2$

10) $(7-3x)^2$

11) $(x^2+4)(x-6)$

12) $(3y^2+5)(6y-7)$

13) $(x-1)(4x-21)$

14) $(2y-1)(3y+8)$

15) $(3x+4y)^2$

16) $(3x-5)(x+3)$

17) $(5y+2)(3y-5)$

18) $(3y-2)(2y-3)$

19) $(4a+1)(3a-5)$

20) $3(5x-4)(2x-3)$

Solving Quadratic Equations by Factoring

1) $x = 0, 5$

2) $x = -2, -7$

3) $z = 7, -5$

4) $a = -3, -9$

5) $x = \pm\dfrac{11}{2}$

6) $x = \dfrac{7}{2}$

7) $x = -1, \dfrac{5}{3}$

8) $x = \pm\dfrac{9}{5}$

9) $x = -1, -6$

10) $x = -8$

11) $y = 0, -8$

12) $x = 3, -4$

13) $x = -\dfrac{1}{2}, \dfrac{4}{3}$

14) $x = -3, 6$

15) $y = \pm\dfrac{10}{3}$

16) $x = -\dfrac{1}{2}, -\dfrac{4}{3}$

17) $x = \dfrac{2}{3}, -1$

18) $x = -1$

19) $x = -2, -\dfrac{1}{2}$

20) $x = 2$

Rational Expressions: Multiplication

1) $\dfrac{2x}{5y}$

2) $\dfrac{5x(x+2)}{6y^2}$

3) $\dfrac{3}{2x^3}$

4) $\dfrac{2a^2}{3}$

5) $\dfrac{3a(a-6)}{2}$

6) $\dfrac{3(x+4)}{2(x-8)}$

7) $\dfrac{4(y+6)}{3(y-2)}$

8) $\dfrac{1}{x+7}$

9) 1

10) $\dfrac{x+4}{x+2}$

11) $\dfrac{4x}{x-2}$

12) $\dfrac{(y+3)(y-3)}{y+4}$

13) $\dfrac{(x+2)(x-2)}{(x+1)(x-1)}$

14) $\dfrac{24}{(y-3)(y+1)}$

15) $(x+1)(x-1)$

16) $\dfrac{(a-5)(a-3)}{(a+2)(a-4)}$

17) $\dfrac{45}{2x^3}$

18) $\dfrac{8x}{y^2}$

19) 1

20) $\dfrac{(x+5)(y+4)}{(x-5)(y-4)}$

Rational Expressions: Division

1a) $\dfrac{x+2}{3x-5}$

1b) $\dfrac{y-7}{2y-9}$

2a) $\dfrac{8x}{15y^2}$

2b) $\dfrac{9a^2}{7b^2}$

3a) $\dfrac{2}{3xy}$

3b) $\dfrac{y}{x}$

4a) $\dfrac{ab}{3}$

4b) $\dfrac{3xy}{4}$

5) $a(2a+7)$

6) $\dfrac{(x+4)(x+2)}{3}$

7) $\dfrac{y-4}{y+4}$

8) $\dfrac{x+5}{x+4}$

9) $\dfrac{(x+1)(x-7)(x+7)}{3x(x-4)}$

10) $4(x-1)$

11) $\dfrac{3}{16}$

12) $\dfrac{a+1}{a-1}$

Rational Expressions: Add & Subtract

1) $\dfrac{10x}{x+4}$

2) $\dfrac{13y}{y-3}$

3) $\dfrac{26}{3x}$

4) $\dfrac{32+15x^2}{12x^2}$

5) $\dfrac{3y^2-4}{y+1}$

6) $\dfrac{2x-5}{3x-5}$

7) $\dfrac{9y^2-7}{3y^3}$

8) $\dfrac{20a-21}{12a^2}$

9) $\dfrac{-7x^2+8x}{(3x-2)(x+1)}$

10) $\dfrac{a^2+6a}{a^2-16}$

11) $\dfrac{3y^2-8}{6y^2}$

12) $\dfrac{x^2+7x+16}{(x+1)(x+3)(x+4)}$

13) $\dfrac{-2x^2+16x+20}{(x-3)(x+2)(x+2)}$

14) $\dfrac{x^2+12}{(x-3)(x-2)(x+4)}$

15) $\dfrac{a^2+ab+2a+b}{a^2b^2}$

16) $\dfrac{x-14}{(x+2)(x-2)}$

17) $\dfrac{-x^2+8x}{(x+4)(x-4)}$

18) $\dfrac{x^2+10x+11}{(x-7)(x+7)}$

19) $\dfrac{-4x+7}{(x-1)^2}$

20) $\dfrac{7}{t+4}$

Extra Problem Set Answers: Elementary Algebra

Systems of Equations: Graphing

1) a. No
   b. Yes
   c. Yes

2) Intersection is at (3,4)

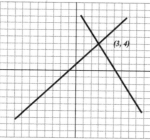

3) Intersection is at (-2,-3)

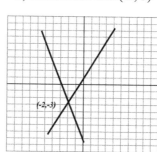

4) Intersection is at (3,-1)

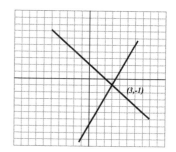

5) Intersection is at (-3,2)

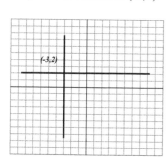

Systems of Equations: The Substitution Method

1) (-3,-4)   2) (2,-7)   3) (5,2)   4) (4,3)   5) (1,3)   6) (-1,1)   7) $(\frac{8}{7}, -\frac{16}{7})$

Systems of Equations: The Elimination Method

1) (5,-4)   2) (-2,2)   3) (3,3)   4) (6,4)   5) (2,2)   6) $(-\frac{21}{25}, -\frac{47}{25})$ 7) (2,-1)

Radicals

1) 12   4) $\sqrt{55}$ 7) $5\sqrt{7}$ 10) $3\sqrt{11}$ 13) $\frac{\sqrt{6}}{2}$ 16) $11\sqrt{11}$ 19) $7\sqrt{6}$

2) 11   5) $\sqrt{42}$ 8) $2\sqrt{17}$ 11) 4   14) $\frac{4}{7}$ 17) $12\sqrt{3}$ 20) $26\sqrt{2}$

3) $4\sqrt{3}$ 6) $6\sqrt{2}$ 9) $3\sqrt{3}$ 12) $\sqrt{6}$ 15) $10\sqrt{5}$ 18) $8\sqrt{7}$

The Pythagorean Theorem

1) $c=10$ 4) $c = \sqrt{34}$ or 5.83   7) $c = \sqrt{106}$ or 10.30   10) $c = \sqrt{113}$ or 10.63

2) $b = 2\sqrt{39}$ or 12.49   5) $b = 2\sqrt{21}$ or 9.17   8) $b = \sqrt{55}$ or 7.42

3) $a = 4\sqrt{6}$ or 9.80   6) $a = 2\sqrt{35}$ or 11.83   9) $a = \sqrt{65}$ or 8.06

Extra Problem Set Answers: Elementary Algebra

The Quadratic Formula

1) $x = \dfrac{4}{3}, 1$

2) $x = \dfrac{1}{2}, -\dfrac{7}{2}$

3) $y = 2 \pm \sqrt{7}$

4) $x = \dfrac{-3 \pm \sqrt{57}}{2}$

5) $x = \pm\sqrt{6}$

6) $x = 5, -2$

7) $x = -2 \pm \sqrt{11}$

8) $x = \dfrac{2 \pm \sqrt{10}}{3}$

9) $x = \dfrac{-1 \pm \sqrt{6}}{2}$

10) $x = \dfrac{1 \pm \sqrt{3}}{2}$

More Word Problems

1) The legs of the triangle are 7.3 inches & 5.3 inches.
2) There were 430 regular tickets sold and 200 student tickets sold.
3) The width of the rectangle is 9 meters and the length is 12 meters.
4) Slice of pizza is $2.00 and a soda is $1.50.
5) The ladder will reach 17.5 feet high.

Extra Problem Sets
Intermediate Algebra

Extra Problem Set: Lesson 22 - Functions and Relations

1. Are these relations functions?

Relation 1		Relation 2		Relation 3		Relation 4		Relation 5	
x	y_1	x	y_2	x	y_3	x	y_4	x	y_5
0	0	2	3	1	1	1	3	1	1
1	1	3	3	1	−1	2	5	2	4
2	2	4	3	2	4	3	7	3	7
3	4	5	3	2	−4	4	9	1	1

2. Determine whether the following graphs are functions.

a.

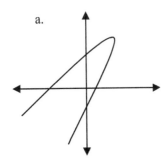

b.

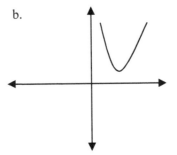

c.

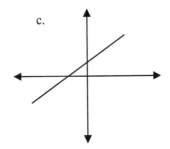

d.

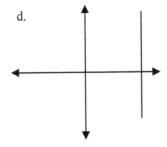

274

Extra Problem Set: Lesson 23 - Function Notation

3. Let $f(x) = -3x - 2$ and $g(x) = 2(x+4)$

    a. Find $f(x) + g(x)$

    d. Find $f(a+2) + g(a+2)$

    b. Find $f(x) - g(x)$

    e. For what value of x is $f(x) = -14$?

    c. Find $f(3) + g(-2)$

    f. For what value of x is $g(x) = -4$?

4. Let $f(x) = 4(x-2)$ and $g(x) = -3(x+7)$

    a. Find $f(x) + g(x)$

    d. Find $f(a-2) + g(a+3)$

    b. Find $f(x) - g(x)$

    e. For what value of x is $f(x) = -10$?

    c. Find $f(5) - g(2)$

    f. For what value of x is $g(x) = -12$?

Extra Problem Set: Lesson 24 - Modeling With Linear Functions

1. A research project has shown a relationship between the number of years of math taken (and passed) from the ninth grade on and average annual earnings. This relationship is shown in the table below.
    a) Develop a scattergram to see if the data are approximately linearly related.

Year	Avg. Annual Earnings (in thousands of dollars)
0	$20
1	$26
2	$38
3	$52
4	$61
5	$68
6	$80

   b) Develop a model that best represents this data.

   c) What might you earn a year if you took 8 years of math?

2. Girl Scout Troop WXYZ sells cookies each year. Their sales record is shown in the table below.
    a) Develop a scattergram to see if the data are approximately linearly related.

Year	Boxes of Cookies
1990	500
1992	525
1994	640
1996	660
1998	760
2000	800
2002	820

b) Develop a model from this data

c) How many boxes will be sold in 2008?

d) When will they sell 1280 boxes?

3. Company XYZ sells widgets. Their sales history is shown in the table below.
   a) Develop a scattergram to see if the data are approximately linearly related.

Year	# of Widgets Sold
1980	300
1985	450
1990	750
1995	850
2000	1100

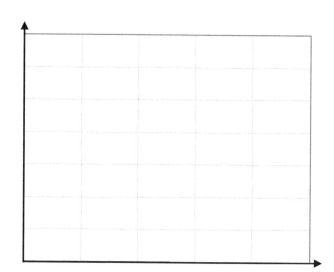

b) Develop a model from this data.

c) How many widgets will be sold in 2005?

d) When will the company sell 1500 widgets?

Extra Problem Set: Lesson 25 -Rational Exponents

Simplify the following:

1. $27^{\frac{2}{3}}$

2. $16^{\frac{3}{4}}$

3. $243^{\frac{3}{5}}$

4. $100^{\frac{3}{2}}$

5. $7^{\frac{2}{3}} \bullet 7^{\frac{4}{3}}$

6. $\dfrac{x^{\frac{4}{5}}}{x^{\frac{1}{3}}}$

7. 6^{-2}

8. $625^{\frac{3}{4}}$

9. $x^{\frac{1}{5}} \bullet x^{\frac{3}{4}}$

10. $(x^{\frac{3}{4}})^{\frac{1}{3}}$

11. $3^{\frac{2}{5}} \bullet 3^{\frac{3}{5}}$

12. $81^{\frac{5}{4}}$

13. $16^{-\frac{1}{2}}$

14. $\left(\dfrac{2}{3}\right)^{-3}$

Extra Problem Set: Lesson 26 - The Basics of Exponential Functions

1. Set up a table of values and sketch the four exponential functions on the graphs on the following page:

$$f(x) = 4^x \qquad g(x) = \left(\frac{1}{3}\right)^x \qquad h(x) = -2(3)^x \qquad j(x) = -4\left(\frac{1}{2}\right)^x$$

x	$f(x)$	$g(x)$	$h(x)$	$j(x)$
−3				
−2				
−1				
0				
1				
2				
3				

Graphs:

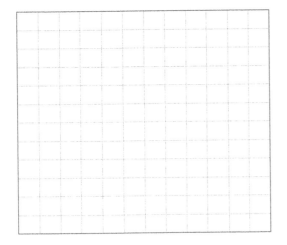

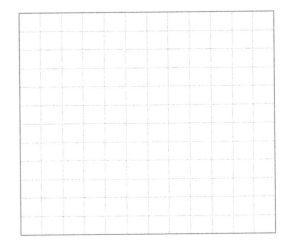

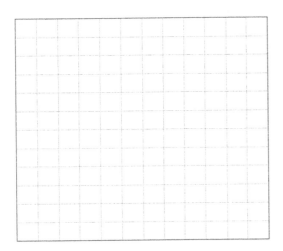

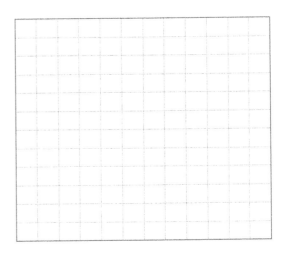

Extra Problem Set: Lesson 27 - More on Exponential Functions

1. Determine if the following functions are linear or exponential and find an equation for each.

x	$f(x)$	$g(x)$	$h(x)$	$j(x)$
−2	−3	1	5	640
−1	−1	4	0	320
0	1	16	−5	160
1	3	64	−10	80
2	5	256	−15	40

$f(x) =$

$g(x) =$

$h(x) =$

$j(x) =$

Extra Problem Set: Lesson 28 - Solving Equations With Constant Exponents

Solve the following equations:

1. $6x^3 = 48$

8. $7x^3 = 70$

2. $3y^2 = 75$

9. $6a^3 - 5 = 13$

3. $2x^2 - 3 = 29$

10. $4x^4 + 7 = 35$

4. $7y^2 + 10 = 38$

11. $3x^3 + 2 = 83$

5. $\dfrac{1}{2}x^2 + \dfrac{1}{5} = \dfrac{11}{5}$

`12. $\dfrac{x^2}{4} - \dfrac{1}{3} = \dfrac{1}{2}$

6. $\dfrac{1}{3}x^2 - \dfrac{2}{5} = \dfrac{119}{15}$

13. $\dfrac{y^2}{15} - \dfrac{2}{3} = \dfrac{2}{5}$

7. $4x^4 = 24$

14. $3x^5 = 16$

Extra Problem Set: Lesson 29 - The Basics of Logarithmic Functions

Find the inverse of the following:

1. $f(x) = 2x + 5$

3. $h(x) = 3^x$

2. $g(x) = -3x - 4$

4. $j(x) = \log_5 x$

Write the following as logarithmic equations:

5. $2^5 = 32$

7. $x^3 = 27$

6. $3^4 = 81$

8. $4^3 = x$

Write the following as exponential equations:

9. $\log_7 49 = 2$

11. $\log_x 81 = 4$

10. $\log_5 125 = 3$

12. $\log_x y = z$

Extra Problem Set: Lesson 30 - Solving Logarithmic Equations

Solve the following equations for *x*:

1. $\log_3 x = 4$

2. $\log_4 x = 3$

3. $\log x = 4$

4. $\log_5 x = 4$

5. $\log_4 x = -3$

6. $\log x = 3$

7. $\log_5 x = 0$

8. $\log_3 x = -2$

9. $\log_2 x = -4$

10. $\log x = -2$

11. $\log_a x = 2$

12. $\log_2 x = -1$

Solve the following for *b*:

13. $\log_b 64 = 6$

14. $\log_b 81 = 4$

Extra Problem Set: Lesson 31 - Properties of Logarithms

Solve the following equations:

1. $5^x = 14$

2. $2^x = 17$

3. $3(4^x) = 27$

4. $7(3^x) = 70$

5. $4^x - 7 = 24$

6. $2 + 3(4^x) = 32$

7. $4^{2x+3} = 15$

8. $5^{3x-2} = 18$

9. $6^{4x-5} = 18$

10. $4^{2x-1} = 9$

Extra Problem Set: Lesson 32 - Natural Logarithms

1. Write in logarithmic format: $e^a = c$

2. Write in exponential format: $\ln 14 = x$

3. Write in exponential format: $\ln 10 = y$

4. Solve for x: $\ln(e^4) = x$

Solve for x using natural log format:

5. $3(5^x) = 21$

6. $3^{4x+5} = 8$

7. $4^{3x-1} = 7$

8. $4(3^x) - 6 = 18$

9. $\ln(6x) = 20$

10. $e^{5x} = 22$

Extra Problem Set: Lesson 33 - The Basics of Quadratic Functions

1. For the function $f(x) = x^2 + 4x - 12$:

    a. Find the x intercept(s)

    b. Find the y intercept

    c. Find the coordinates of the vertex

    d. Find the axis of symmetry

    e. Sketch the graph of the function

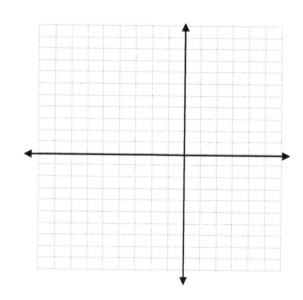

2. For the function $g(x) = -x^2 + 4x + 21$:

    a. Find the x intercept(s)

    b. Find the y intercept

    c. Find the coordinates of the vertex

    d. Find the axis of symmetry

    e. Sketch the graph of the function

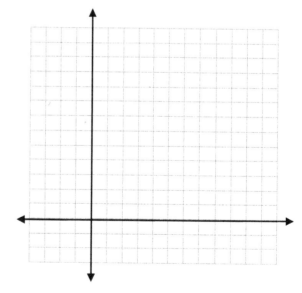

3. For the function $h(x) = x^2 + 5x + 8$:

    a. Find the x intercept(s)

    b. Find the y intercept

    c. Find the coordinates of the vertex

    d. Find the axis of symmetry

    e. Sketch the graph of the function

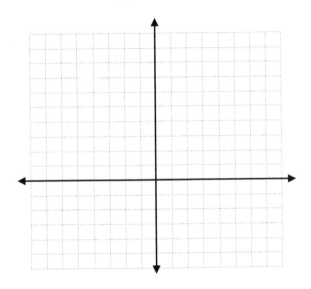

Extra Problem Set: Lesson 34 - Complex Numbers

1. Express the following as a complex number: $\dfrac{4+\sqrt{-29}}{3}$

2. Express the following as a complex number: $\dfrac{6-\sqrt{-7}}{5}$

3. Express the following as a complex number: $\dfrac{7\pm\sqrt{-21}}{3}$

4. Express the following as a complex number in simplest form: $\dfrac{-6+\sqrt{-45}}{3}$

5. Express the following as a complex number in simplest form: $\dfrac{2\pm\sqrt{-121}}{5}$

6. Solve, and write the answer as a complex number in simplest form: $x^2 + 3x + 12 = 0$

7. Solve, and write the answer as a complex number in simplest form: $5x^2 - 6x + 5 = 0$

8. Solve, and write the answer as a complex number in simplest form: $4x^2 = 7x - 8$

9. Solve, and write the answer as a complex number in simplest form: $x^2 - 3x + 10 = 0$

Extra Problem Set: Lesson 35 - Solving Non-Linear Systems of Equations

1. Solve the system of equations: $y = x^2 - 2$

$$y = 3x - 2$$

2. Solve the system of equations: $y = x^2 - 6$

$$y = -7x - 12$$

3. Solve the system of equations: $y = x^2 - 2x + 4$

$$2x + y = 13$$

4. Solve the system of equations: $x^2 + y^2 = 10$

$$4x^2 + 2y^2 = 22$$

5. Solve the system of equations: $x^2 + y^2 = 20$

$$3x^2 - y^2 = -4$$

Extra Problem Set: Lesson 36 - The Basics of Rational Functions

Find the domain of the following functions:

1. $f(x) = \dfrac{x-6}{x+4}$

2. $g(x) = \dfrac{x^2+3x+4}{x-5}$

3. $h(x) = \dfrac{x+3}{x^2+5x+4}$

4. $j(x) = \dfrac{2x-3}{x^2+5x}$

5. $k(x) = \dfrac{3x+7}{x^2-11x+28}$

Simplify and find the domains of the following functions:

6. $f(x) = \dfrac{3x+12}{x^2-2x-24}$

7. $g(x) = \dfrac{x^2+2x-8}{x^2-16}$

8. $h(x) = \dfrac{x^2-7x-18}{x^2-5x-36}$

9. $j(x) = \dfrac{x^2-5x}{x^3-11x^2+30x}$

10. $k(x) = \dfrac{4x+8}{x^2+12x+20}$

Extra Problem Set: Lesson 37 - Solving Rational Equations

Solve the following equations:

1. $\dfrac{3}{x} + 3 = 7 - \dfrac{21}{x}$

2. $\dfrac{x}{x+3} - \dfrac{2}{x-7} = \dfrac{-20}{x^2 - 4x - 21}$

3. $\dfrac{x-4}{x-7} = \dfrac{3}{x-7}$

4. $\dfrac{4}{x^2 + 3x + 2} + \dfrac{2}{x^2 + 5x + 6} = \dfrac{x^2 - 2}{(x+1)(x+2)(x+3)}$

5. $8 + \dfrac{10}{x} = \dfrac{3}{x^2}$

Extra Problem Set: Lesson 38 - The Basics of Radical Functions

1. Determine the domain and range and sketch $f(x) = 2\sqrt{x+6}$.

    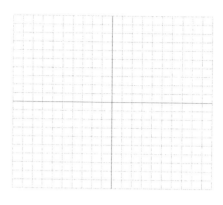

2. Determine the domain and range and sketch $g(x) = 3\sqrt{x-4}$.

    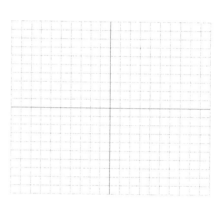

3. Determine the domain and range and sketch $h(x) = -4\sqrt{x+3} + 2$.

    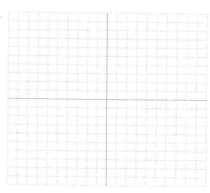

4. Determine the domain and range and sketch $j(x) = -3\sqrt{x-2} - 4$.

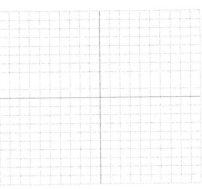

5. Determine the domain and range and sketch $k(x) = 2\sqrt{x+5} - 3$.

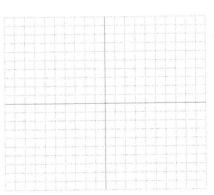

Extra Problem Set: Lesson 39 - Solving Radical Equations

Solve the following equations:

1. $\sqrt{x} = 8$

2. $\sqrt{x} + 6 = 9$

3. $-6 + \sqrt{x} = -2$

4. $14 = \sqrt{x} + 3$

5. $\sqrt{3x - 2} = \sqrt{5x - 12}$

6. $\sqrt{7x - 5} = \sqrt{3x + 7}$

7. $\sqrt{3x - 8} = x - 4$

8. $\sqrt{6x - 26} = x - 3$

9. $\sqrt{3x - 17} + 5 = x$

10. $\sqrt{6x - 11} = x - 3$

Extra Problem Set Answers: Intermediate Algebra

Lesson 22 - Relations and Functions

1. Relation 1 – Yes   Relation 2 – Yes   Relation 3 – No   Relation 4 – Yes   Relation 5 – Yes

2a. No   b. Yes   c. Yes   d. No

Lesson 23 - Function Notation

1a. $-x+6$ b. $-5x-10$ c. -7 d. $-a+4$ e. $x=4$ f. $x=-6$

2a. $x-29$ b. $7x+13$ c. 39   d. $a-46$ e. $x=-\dfrac{1}{2}$ f. $x=-3$

Lesson 24 - Modeling with Linear Functions

1a) The scattergram for the research project is shown below.

Year	Avg. Annual Earnings (in thousands of dollars)
0	$20
1	$26
2	$38
3	$52
4	$61
5	$68
6	$80

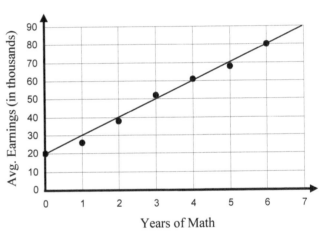

Years of Math

b) Using points (0, 20) and (6, 80), the model is: $y=10x+20$

d) If you took 8 years of math, the model predicts your earnings would be $100,000 $(y=100)$.

2a) The scattergram for the Girl Scout cookie sales is shown below.

Year	Boxes of Cookies
1990	500
1992	540
1994	640
1996	660
1998	760
2000	800
2002	820

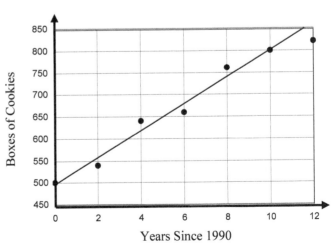

Years Since 1990

296

b) Using points (1990, 500) and (2000, 800), and letting the year 1990 be represented by 0, the model is: $y = 30x + 500$.

c) There will be 1040 boxes sold in the year 2008.

d) They will sell 1280 boxes in the year 2016.

3a) The scattergram for Company XYZ's sales is shown below.

Year	No. of Widgets Sold
1980	300
1986	450
1990	750
1995	850
2000	1100

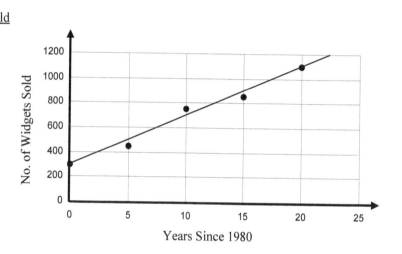

b) Using points (1980, 300) and (2000, 1100), and letting the year 1980 be represented by 0, the model is: $y = 40x + 300$.

c) There will be 1300 widgets sold in 2005.

d) The company will sell 1500 widgets in 2010.

Lesson 25 - Rational Exponents

1. 9

2. 8

3. 27

4. 1000

5. 49

6. $x^{\frac{7}{15}}$

7. $\dfrac{1}{36}$

8. 125

9. $x^{\frac{19}{20}}$

10. $x^{\frac{1}{4}}$

11. 3

12. 243

13. $\dfrac{1}{4}$

14. $\dfrac{27}{8}$

Lesson 26 - The Basics of Exponential Functions

1.

x	$f(x)$	$g(x)$	$h(x)$	$j(x)$
-3	$\dfrac{1}{64}$	27	$-\dfrac{2}{27}$	-32
-2	$\dfrac{1}{16}$	9	$-\dfrac{2}{9}$	-16
-1	$\dfrac{1}{4}$	3	$-\dfrac{2}{3}$	-8
0	1	1	-2	-4
1	4	$\dfrac{1}{3}$	-6	-2
2	16	$\dfrac{1}{9}$	-18	-1
3	64	$\dfrac{1}{27}$	-54	$-\dfrac{1}{2}$

$f(x)$

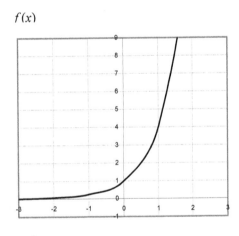

$g(x)$

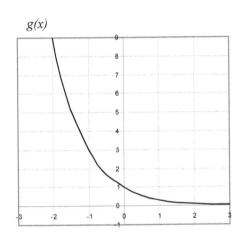

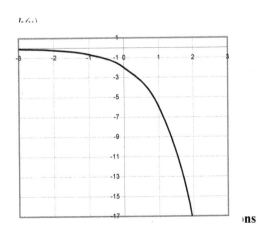

$j(x)$

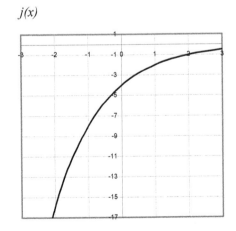

ins

298

$f(x)$ is a linear function, $f(x) = 2x + 1$

$g(x)$ is an exponential function, $g(x) = 16(4)^x$

$h(x)$ is a linear funciton, $h(x) = -5x - 5$

$j(x)$ is an exponential function, $j(x) = 160\left(\dfrac{1}{2}\right)^x$

Lesson 28 - Solving Equations With Constant Exponents

1. $x = 2$

2. $y = \pm 5$

3. $x = \pm 4$

4. $y = \pm 2$

5. $x = \pm 2$

6. $x = \pm 5$

7. $x = \pm 6^{\frac{1}{4}}$

8. $x = 10^{\frac{1}{3}}$

9. $a = 3^{\frac{1}{3}}$

10. $x = \pm 7^{\frac{1}{4}}$

11. $x = 3$

12. $x = \pm\left(\dfrac{10}{3}\right)^{\frac{1}{2}}$

13. $y = \pm 4$

14. $x = \left(\dfrac{16}{3}\right)^{\frac{1}{5}}$

Lesson 29 - The Basics of Logarithmic Functions

1. $f^{-1}(x) = \dfrac{x-5}{2}$

2. $g^{-1}(x) = \dfrac{x+4}{-3}$

3. $h^{-1}(x) = \log_3 x$

4. $j^{-1}(x) = 5^x$

5. $\log_2 32 = 5$

6. $\log_3 81 = 4$

7. $\log_x 27 = 3$

8. $\log_4 x = 3$

9. $7^2 = 49$

10. $5^3 = 125$

11. $x^4 = 81$

12. $x^z = y$

Lesson 30 - Solving Logarithmic Equations

1. $x = 81$

2. 2. $x = 64$

3. $x = 10,000$

4. $x = 625$

5. $x = \dfrac{1}{64}$

6. $x = 1000$

7. $x = 1$

8. $b = \dfrac{1}{9}$

9. $x = \dfrac{1}{16}$

10. $x = \dfrac{1}{100}$

11. $x = a^2$

12. $x = \dfrac{1}{2}$

13. $b = 2$

14. $b = 3$

Lesson 31 - Properties of Logarithms

1. $x = \dfrac{\log 14}{\log 5}$ 6. $x = \dfrac{\log 10}{\log 4}$

2. $x = \dfrac{\log 17}{\log 2}$ 7. $x = \dfrac{\dfrac{\log 15}{\log 4} - 3}{2}$

3. $x = \dfrac{\log 9}{\log 4}$ 8. $x = \dfrac{\dfrac{\log 18}{\log 5} + 2}{3}$

4. $x = \dfrac{\log 10}{\log 3}$ 9. $x = \dfrac{\dfrac{\log 18}{\log 6} + 5}{4}$

5. $x = \dfrac{\log 31}{\log 4}$ 10. $x = \dfrac{\dfrac{\log 9}{\log 4} + 1}{2}$

Lesson 32 - Natural Logarithms

1. $\ln c = a$ 6. $x = \dfrac{\dfrac{\ln 8}{\ln 3} - 5}{4}$

2. $e^x = 14$ 7. $x = \dfrac{\dfrac{\ln 7}{\ln 4} + 1}{3}$

3. $e^y = 10$ 8. $x = \dfrac{\ln 6}{\ln 3}$

4. $x = 4$ 9. $x = \dfrac{e^{20}}{6}$

5. $x = \dfrac{\ln 7}{\ln 5}$ 10. $x = \dfrac{\ln 22}{5}$

Lesson 33 - The Basics of Quadratic Functions

1. For the function $f(x) = x^2 + 4x - 12$:

1a. The x intercepts are $(-6, 0)$ and $(2, 0)$.

1b. The y intercept is $(0, -12)$.

1c. The coordinates of the vertex are $(-2, -16)$.

1d. The equation of the axis of symmetry is $x = -2$.

1e. The graph of the function:

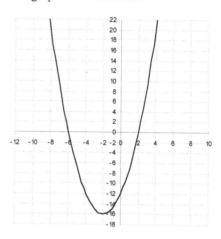

2. For the function $g(x) = -x^2 + 4x + 21$:

2a. The x intercepts are $(-3, 0)$ and $(7, 0)$.

2b. The y intercept is $(0, 21)$.

2c. The coordinates of the vertex are $(2, 25)$.

2d. The equation of the axis of symmetry is $x = 2$.

2e. The graph of the function:

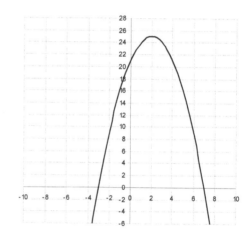

3. For the function $h(x) = x^2 + 5x + 8$

3a. No x intercepts.

3b. The y intercept is $(0, 8)$

3c. The coordinates of the vertex are $(-2.5, 1.75)$

3d. The equation of the axis of symmetry is $x = -2.5$

3e. The graph of the function:

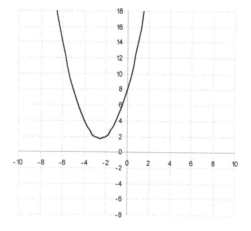

301

Lesson 34 - Complex Numbers

1. $\dfrac{4}{3}+\dfrac{\sqrt{29}}{3}i$

2. $\dfrac{6}{5}-\dfrac{\sqrt{7}}{5}i$

3. $\dfrac{7}{3}\pm\dfrac{\sqrt{21}}{3}i$

4. $-2+\sqrt{5}i$

5. $\dfrac{2}{5}\pm\dfrac{11}{5}i$

6. $-\dfrac{3}{2}\pm\dfrac{\sqrt{39}}{2}i$

7. $\dfrac{3}{5}\pm\dfrac{4}{5}i$

8. $\dfrac{7}{8}\pm\dfrac{\sqrt{79}}{8}i$

9. $\dfrac{3}{2}\pm\dfrac{\sqrt{31}}{2}i$

Lesson 35 - Solving Non-Linear Systems of Equations

1. $(0,-2)$ and $(3,7)$
2. $(-1,-5)$ and $(-6,30)$
3. $(3,7)$ and $(-3,19)$
4. $(1,-3),\ (-1,3),\ (1,3),$ and $(-1,-3)$
5. $(2,4),\ (-2,4),\ (2,-4),$ and $(-2,-4)$

Lesson 36 – The Basics of Rational Functions

1. The Domain is the set of all real numbers except $x=-4$.
2. The Domain is the set of all real numbers except $x=5$.
3. The Domain is the set of all real numbers except $x=-1$ and -4.
4. The Domain is the set of all real numbers except $x=0$ and -5.
5. The Domain is the set of all real numbers except $x=4$ and 7.

6. $f(x)=\dfrac{3}{x-6}$ The Domain is the set of all real numbers except $x=6$ and -4

7. $g(x)=\dfrac{x-2}{x-4}$ The Domain is the set of all real numbers except $x=4$ and -4.

8. $h(x)=\dfrac{x+2}{x+4}$ The Domain is the set of all real numbers except $x=9$ and -4

9. $j(x)=\dfrac{1}{x-6}$ The Domain is the set of all real numbers except $x=0,\ 5,$ and 6.

10. $k(x)=\dfrac{4}{x+10}$ The Domain is the set of all real numbers except $x=-2$ and -10

Lesson 37 - Solving Rational Equations

1. $x=6$
2. $x=2$ is the only valid solution.
3. Extraneous solution.
4. $x=8$ is the only valid solution.
5. $x=-\dfrac{3}{2},$ and $\dfrac{1}{4}$

Lesson 38 - The Basics of Radical Functions

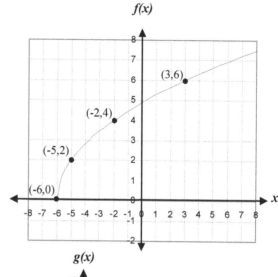

$f(x)$

1. The Domain is the set of all real numbers ≥ -6.
    The Range is the set of all real numbers ≥ 0.

    Sketch:

x	$f(x)$
-6	0
-5	2
-2	4
3	6

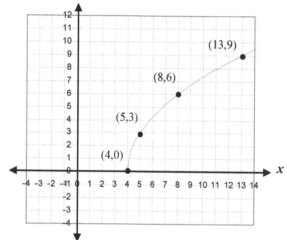

$g(x)$

2. The Domain is the set of all real numbers ≥ 4
    The Range is the set of all real numbers ≥ 0

    Sketch:

x	$g(x)$
4	0
5	3
8	6
13	9

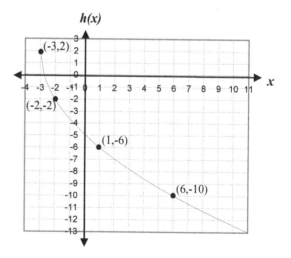

$h(x)$

3. The Domain is the set of all real numbers ≥ -3.
    The Range is the set of all real numbers ≤ 2.

    Sketch:

x	$h(x)$
-3	2
-2	-2
1	-6
6	-10

303

4. The Domain is the set of all real numbers ≥ 2
   The Range is the set of all real numbers ≤ -4

   Sketch:

x	$j(x)$
2	-4
3	-7
6	-10
11	-13

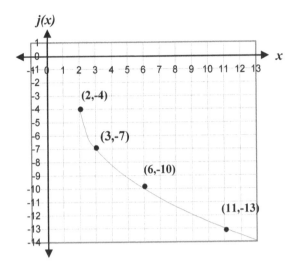

5. The Domain is the set of all real numbers ≥ -5.
   The Range is the set of all real numbers ≥ -3.

   Sketch:

x	$k(x)$
-5	-3
-4	-1
-1	1
4	3

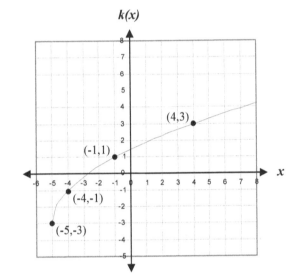

Lesson 39 - Solving Radical Equations

1. $x = 64$
2. $x = 9$
3. $x = 16$
4. $x = 121$
5. $x = 5$

6. $x = 3$
7. $x = 8$ ($x = 3$ is not a valid solution)
8. $x = 5, 7$
9. $x = 6, 7$
10. $x = 10$ ($x = 2$ is not a valid solution)

Appendix A

Elementary Algebra – Rules to Remember

Solving a Formula for a Given Variable
1. Identify the letter to be solved for.
2. Clear the equation of fractions or decimals.
3. Collect like terms, if necessary.

Use the addition property to get all terms with the given letter on one side of the equation and all other terms on the other side.

Solving Inequalities
If you multiply or divide by a negative number, you must reverse (flip) the inequality sign.

Slope $(m) = \dfrac{rise}{run} = \dfrac{y_2 - y_1}{x_2 - x_1}$

Slope-intercept Form
$y = mx + b$

Rules for Exponents

$a^m \bullet a^n = a^{m+n}$

$\dfrac{a^m}{a^n} = a^{m-n}$

$(a^m)^n = a^{mn}$

$(ab)^n = a^n b^n$

$a^{-n} = \dfrac{1}{a^n}$

$a^1 = a$

$a^0 = 1$

$\left(\dfrac{a}{b}\right)^n = \dfrac{a^n}{b^n}$

Perpendicular Lines
The product of slopes = -1

Parallel Lines
Have equal slopes

Scientific Notation

Scientific notation is used to write very large and very small numbers. The format used is:

$M \times 10^n$ Where $1 \leq M < 10$ and n is an integer

Special Products of Binomials

$(A + B)(A - B) = A^2 - B^2$

$(A + B)^2 = A^2 + 2AB + B^2$

$(A - B)^2 = A^2 - 2AB + B^2$

Factoring Process

- Look for a common factor
- Factor completely
- Check your answer by multiplying

Guidelines for Recognizing Trinomial Squares

In order for an expression to be a trinomial square like:
$$A^2 + 2AB + B^2 \quad \text{or} \quad A^2 - 2AB + B^2$$

- the two terms, A^2 and B^2, must be squares,
- there must be no negative sign before A^2 and B^2, and
- if you multiply A and B, and then double it, you should get the middle term.

Steps for Factoring $ax^2 + bx + c$ Using Grouping

Step 1: Factor out a common factor, if one exists.

Step 2: Multiply a times c.

Step 3: Factor ac so that the sum of the factors (if sign of c is positive) or the difference of the factors (if sign of c is negative) is b.

Step 4: Split the middle term using the factors found in step 3

Step 5: Factor by grouping

The Product Rule for Radicals

$$\sqrt{A} \bullet \sqrt{B} = \sqrt{AB}$$
$$\text{and}$$
$$\sqrt{AB} = \sqrt{A} \bullet \sqrt{B}$$

Quotient Rule for Radicals

$$\frac{\sqrt{A}}{\sqrt{B}} = \sqrt{\frac{A}{B}} \quad \text{and} \quad \sqrt{\frac{A}{B}} = \frac{\sqrt{A}}{\sqrt{B}}$$

Standard Form

$ax^2 + bx + c = 0$

The Quadratic Formula

$$x = \frac{-b \pm \sqrt{b^2 - 4ac}}{2a}$$

The Pythagorean Theorem:
$$c^2 = a^2 + b^2$$

Intermediate Algebra – Rules to Remember

Vertical Line Test

If a vertical line intersects the graph at more than one point than it is not a function. This **vertical line test** helps to show that any linear equation is a function except the type $x = c$ where c is a constant since this represents a vertical line itself.

Base Multiplier Property

For an exponential function in the standard form $y = ab^x$, as the value of the independent variable x, increases by 1, the value of the dependent variable y is **multiplied** by the base b.

Exponential/Logarithm Relationship

$y = a^x$ is the same as: $\log_a y = x$

Power Property

$$\log_b(x^p) = p \log_b x$$

Properties of Natural Log

$\ln 1 = 0$

$\ln e = 1$

$\ln a^x = x \ln a$

Finding the Domain of a Functions

For a function of the form: $f(x) = a\sqrt{radicand} + b$,

the domain is the solution to: $radicand \geq 0$

the range is the set of all real numbers $\geq b$ if a is positive
or the set of all real numbers $\leq b$ if a is negative.